COMPUTER NUMBERING SYSTEMS

AND BINARY ARITHMETIC

COMPUTER NUMBERING SYSTEMS AND BINARY ARITHMETIC

A Programed Text

TRAINING SYSTEMS, INC.
AND STANLEY L. LEVINE

JOHN F. RIDER PUBLISHER, INC., NEW YORK

a division of HAYDEN PUBLISHING COMPANY, INC.

Second Printing, 1970

Copyright © 1965

TRAINING SYSTEMS, INC.

Library of Congress Catalog Card Number

64-21444

Printed in the United States of America

Preface

Computers and automation are playing a more signifi-
cant part in our daily lives. Applications of data proc-
essing are becoming extensive and the need for qualified
persons is growing.

The heart of a computer functioning requires the use
of the binary numbering system and to a lesser degree the
octal numbering system. These systems are comparable
to our decimal system. This book will teach the student
these different numbering systems and how to convert
from one to another. It will also teach the student how
to add, subtract, multiply and divide in the binary numbering system.

The course is designed for those who know nothing of
the binary or octal system. No knowledge of computers
is necessary. It is a beginning course to introduce students to numbering systems and binary arithmetic. It can
be used as a "self tutor" by the student or as "remedial"
or "extension" material by the teacher.

The author wishes to thank the many students from
school and industry who provided feedback to improve
and evaluate this course prior to its publication.

Stanley L. Levine

NTENTS
face
w to Use This Book

Chapters

How to Use This Book

This book is divided into five chapters, the first four are programed; the fifth is a summarized reference and is not programed.

Each chapter has an introductory page.

The remaining pages are each divided into four numbered areas called frames.

NUMBERS

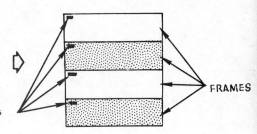

FRAMES

Each frame provides information and almost always will require the student to respond to a question. The correct answer to the question appears on the back of the page. The student should <u>read</u> the information, <u>write</u> his response to the question, and then <u>check</u> his response with the correct one on the back of the page.

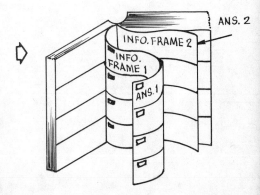

ANS. 2

INFO. FRAME 2

INFO. FRAME 1

ANS. 1

5. All frames are numbered in sequential order. Following this order the student will progress along the top row of frames to the last page of chapter I, then through the second row of frames, the third row and then the fourth. At the end of each row he will be instructed where to go. After chapter I is completed the student will go to chapter II, then chapter III, chapter IV and lastly chapter V. Follow all directions that are given.

CHAPTERS

We hope that you enjoy this programed text.

Chapter I Introduction

Understanding numbering system concepts is important as a basis upon which a knowledge of math and science may grow. Chapter I describes the decimal, octal, and binary numbering systems as well as the symbols of each. It also tells why the binary system is most applicable to digital computers.

Chapter Outline

I Introduction
1. Numbering Systems
2. Why use Binary System in Digital Computers

NOW, TURN THE PAGE AND READ FRAME 1 OF CHAPTER I.

NOTES

1

Numbering Systems

GO TO FRAME 2 ON THE FOLLOWING PAGE

9

Is 485 in the OCTAL system?

17

Numbers in the BINARY SYSTEM larger than 1 are made of combinations of 0 and 1. For example the number after 1 is 10 because 2 through 9 are NOT in the BINARY system. Is 11 in the BINARY SYSTEM?

25

Circle the numbers whose BASE is 2.

$$74_8 \qquad 10_2 \qquad 11_8 \qquad 1_{10} \qquad 1000_2$$

3

1

9

No

17

Yes

25

10_2 1000_2

4

2

There are many different systems of numbering. The one we are familiar with is the DECIMAL SYSTEM.

DECIMAL means "based on" 10.

The system is called the DECIMAL SYSTEM because it is made up of ___ different symbols.

CORRECT RESPONSE IS ON BACK OF THIS PAGE

10

Is 485 in the DECIMAL SYSTEM?

18

Which of the following are in the BINARY SYSTEM?

    (a)   000

    (b)   101

    (c)   123

    (d)   102

26

Circle the numbers in the OCTAL SYSTEM.

$$73_8 \qquad 10_2 \qquad 11_8 \qquad 1_{10} \qquad 1000_2$$

5

10

GO TO NEXT FRAME ON THE FOLLOWING PAGE ▷

10

Yes

18

(a)   000

(b)   101

26

73_8 11_8

3

The following are the 10 symbols that we are familiar with:

1.) 0	4.) 3	7.) 6	10.) 9
2.) 1	5.) 4	8.) 7	
3.) 2	6.) 5	9.) 8	

These ten symbols, 0 and 1 through 9, make up the _____ numbering system.

CORRECT RESPONSE IS ON BACK OF THIS PAGE

11

Which of the following is in the OCTAL system?

(a) 9

(b) 183

(c) 27

(d) 1326

19

Fill in the Blanks:

System	Number of Different Symbols
DECIMAL	_____
OCTAL	_____
BINARY	_____

27

Why Use Binary System in Digital Computers

GO TO NEXT FRAME

DECIMAL

11

(c) 27

(d) 1326

19

System	Number of Different Symbols
DECIMAL	10
OCTAL	8
BINARY	2

27

4

Numbers in the DECIMAL system larger than 9 are made of combinations of these ten symbols.

> 10 is made of 1 and 0.
> 48 is made of 4 and 8.

Is 4,327 a number in the DECIMAL system?

12

DECIMAL means _____ .

OCTAL means _____ .

20

Fill in the Blanks:

System	Write the Different Symbols
DECIMAL	_____
OCTAL	_____
BINARY	_____

28

Digital computers consist of electronic circuits. In these circuits electricity is either <u>flowing</u> or <u>not-flowing</u>. This represents two states of operation.

GO TO NEXT FRAME

Yes

"based on" 10

"based on" 8

System	Write the Different Symbols
DECIMAL	0, 1, 2, 3, 4, 5, 6, 7, 8, 9
OCTAL	0, 1, 2, 3, 4, 5, 6, 7
BINARY	0, 1

5

Write the 10 symbols of the DECIMAL NUMBERING SYSTEM.

13

Write the 8 symbols of the OCTAL SYSTEM.

21

Name the three numbering systems that we have discussed and the number of different symbols in each system.

29

In computer circuits, there are some electron tubes. They are either conducting or not conducting. This also represents _____ states of operation.

11

0	5
1	6
2	7
3	8
4	9

0	4
1	5
2	6
3	7

DECIMAL - 10

OCTAL - 8

BINARY - 2

two

6

Another numbering system is called the OCTAL SYSTEM. <u>OCTAL</u> means "based on" <u>8</u>.

Therefore, there are ___ different symbols in the OCTAL SYSTEM.

14

<u>BINARY</u> means <u>2</u>.

A numbering system using <u>2</u> different symbols is the _____ system.

22

The number of different symbols of any system is called the BASE of that system.

      <u>10</u> is the <u>BASE</u> of the DECIMAL system.

      <u>8</u> is the <u>BASE</u> of the OCTAL system.

      ___ is the <u>BASE</u> of the BINARY system.

30

Switches and relays are "ON" or "OFF". This is another electronic example representing _____ of operation.

6

8

14

BINARY

22

2

30

two states

7

The following are the 8 symbols of the OCTAL SYSTEM.
    1.) 0   4.) 3   7.) 6
    2.) 1   5.) 4   8.) 7
    3.) 2   6.) 5

The eight symbols, 0 and 1 through 7 make up the _____
numbering system.

15

The BINARY SYSTEM uses the symbols 0 and 1. The numbers 1, 10,
10110, and 10010001 are all in the BINARY system because only
_____ different symbols are used.

23

10, 8, and 2 are the _____ of the systems that we have
discussed.

31

Becuuse the electronic digital computer operates basically in two
distinct states, the best numbering system to be used should consist of
two symbols. This system is the _____ numbering system.

7

OCTAL

15

2

23

BASES

31

BINARY

8

Numbers in the OCTAL SYSTEM larger than 7 are made of combinations of 0 through 7. For example, the number after 7 is 10 because 8 and 9 do not exist in this system. Is 34 in the OCTAL system?

16

Write the 2 symbols of the BINARY NUMBERING SYSTEM.

24

Numbers in the DECIMAL system are written:
$$210_{10}, \quad 15_{10}, \quad 1386_{10}$$

Numbers in the OCTAL system are written:
$$35_8, \quad 6342_8, \quad 6_8$$

Write the following numbers for the BINARY system:
10, 101, 11001

32

The BINARY system is used in digital computers because of the two states exhibited by _____ circuits.

8

Yes

16

0, 1

24

10_2, 101_2, 11001_2

32

Electronic

GO TO FRAME 9 ON PAGE 3

GO TO FRAME 17 ON PAGE 3

GO TO FRAME 25 ON PAGE 3

GO TO CHAPTER II ON NEXT PAGE

NOTES

The decimal numbering system is familiar to all of us. However, digital computers use the binary system and to a lesser degree the octal system. The information fed to the computer is in the decimal system and must be converted to the systems used by the computer. Chapter II teaches the student to convert between the decimal, binary and octal systems of numbers. This means, "what number in one system has the same value as a certain number in the other system". For example, "what number in the binary system has the same value as 15 in the decimal system". The answer is 1111. Therefore, 15 in the decimal system is the same as 1111 in the binary system. The last portion of this chapter concerns itself with binary coded decimals.

Chapter Outline

II   Conversion Between Systems
1. Decimal to Binary
2. Decimal to Octal
3. Binary to Decimal
4. Octal to Decimal
5. Binary to Octal
6. Octal to Binary
7. Binary Coded Decimal.

NOW, TURN THE PAGE AND READ FRAME 1 OF CHAPTER II.

NOTES

Decimal to Binary

GO TO NEXT FRAME

29

We will often see a number like this: 10^2. The raised number two$^{(2)}$ is called an exponent.

The exponent of 10^3 is 3.

The exponent of 10^4 is ___.

57

Expand 1 1 1 $= 1(2^0) + 1(2^1) + 1(2^2)$

Multiply $\quad = 1(1) \ + 1(2) \ + 1(4)$

$\quad\quad\quad\quad = 1 \quad + 2 \quad + 4$

Add $\quad\quad = 7$

GO TO NEXT FRAME

85

Converting a number in the OCTAL system to one in the BINARY system is the reverse procedure to converting from the BINARY to the OCTAL system.

GO TO NEXT FRAME

1

29

4

57

85

24

Different numbers in different numbering systems have the SAME VALUE.

For example:

DECIMAL 9
OCTAL 11 } All have the same value.
BINARY 1001

GO TO NEXT FRAME

30

Any number may have an exponent.

The exponent of 5^3 is _3_ .

The exponent of 8^6 is ___ .

58

Convert the BINARY number 101001 to the DECIMAL equivalent.

Expand 101001 = $1(2^0) + 0(2^1) + 0(2^2) + 1(2^3) + 0(2^4) + 1(2^5)$

Multiply = $1(1) + 0(2) + 0(4) + 1(8) + 0(16) + 1(32)$

Add = _____

86

To convert an OCTAL number to the BINARY equivalent, each symbol is converted to a BINARY NUMBER (as if the symbol were in the DECIMAL SYSTEM)

For example:

3 = 011

GO TO NEXT FRAME

2

30

6

58

41

86

26

We will learn how to easily find the number in one system that has the same value as a number in another system. This operation is called CONVERSION.

GO TO NEXT FRAME

31

In the following: 10^8, 8^4, 3^1, 6^0 ;

8, 4, 1, and 0 are called _____ .

59

Convert the BINARY number 10110 to the DECIMAL equivalent.

Expand $10110 = 0(2^0) + 1(2^1) + 1(2^2) + 0(2^3) + 1(2^4)$

Multiply $= 0(\_) + 1(\_) + 1(\_) + 0(\_) + 1(\_)$ } Fill in

Add $= \_\_\_\_$ } the blanks

87

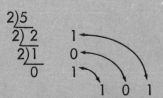

Therefore, 5 in the OCTAL SYSTEM = 101 in the BINARY system.

GO TO NEXT FRAME

exponents

$$= 0(\underline{1}) + 1(\underline{2}) + 1(\underline{4}) + 0(\underline{8}) + 1(\underline{16})$$
$$= \underline{\underline{22}}$$

4

There is a standard procedure of converting a DECIMAL number to a number in a system with a <u>smaller</u> BASE.

The BASE of the BINARY system is _____ (smaller, larger) than the base of the DECIMAL system.

32

The exponent tells us how many times the number is to be multiplied by itself. ① ② ③ ④

$$10^2 = 10 \times 10$$
$$8^3 = 8 \times 8 \times 8$$
$$5^4 = \text{_____}$$

60

Convert the BINARY number 101 to the DECIMAL equivalent.

Expand 101 = _____

Multiply   = _____

Add   = _____

88

Convert 35_8 to the BINARY system equivalent number.

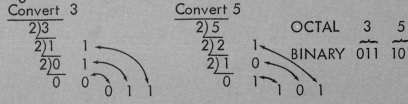

35 in the OCTAL system equals _____ in the BINARY system.

29

smaller

$$5^4 = \underline{\overset{①\;②\;③\;④}{5 \times 5 \times 5 \times 5}}$$

$$
\begin{aligned}
101 &= 1(2^0) + 0(2^1) + 1(2^2) \\
&= 1 \quad\;\; + 0 \quad\;\; + 4 \\
&= 5
\end{aligned}
$$

011101

5

Let us find the BINARY EQUIVALENT (number with same value) of a
DECIMAL NUMBER. This is done by _____ the decimal
number into a BINARY number.

33

$$10^2 = 10 \times 10 \qquad = 100$$
$$8^3 = 8 \times 8 \times 8 = 512$$
$$2^4 = \underline{\hspace{2cm}} = \underline{\hspace{1cm}}$$

61

CONVERSION BETWEEN SYSTEMS

Octal to Decimal

GO TO NEXT FRAME

89

Convert 62_8 to the BINARY system equivalent number.

converting

$$2^4 = \underline{2 \times 2 \times 2 \times 2} = \underline{16}$$

```
2)6              2)2
2)3    0         2)1    0
2)1    1         2)0    1
  0    1           0    0

     110              010


          110010
```

There are two steps in converting a DECIMAL number to an equivalent number in a system with a smaller base.

STEP 1.   Divide the DECIMAL number by the base of the other system and record the remainder.

Example

$$2 \overline{)\ 138} \leftarrow \text{decimal no.}$$

↑
base

What is the Base of the BINARY system?

34

Any number with an exponent of 0 is equal to 1.

2^0, 8^0, 10^0, 5^0 all equal _____.

62

The DECIMAL value of any number in the OCTAL system is

(Symbol) × (Base 8) ^{Place}

$8^0 = 1$ $8^3 = 512$
$8^1 = 8$ $8^4 = 4096$
$8^2 = 64$

GO TO NEXT FRAME

90

Convert 71_8 to the BINARY equivalent.

2

1

```
2)7                      2)1
 2)3    1                 2)0    1
  2)1   1                  2)0   0
    0   1                    0   0

      111                      001
```

111001

STEP 1   Example   ▷   2)12

   ①   What is the DECIMAL number?

   ②   What is the BASE of the smaller numbering system?

35

$$10^2 = 10 \times 10 = 100$$
$$10^1 = 10$$
$$10^0 = \underline{\hspace{2cm}}$$

63

We have learned to convert a binary number to its decimal equivalent.

The same THREE steps are used to convert an OCTAL NUMBER into its equivalent DECIMAL number. These steps are:

   ① _____

   ② _____

   ③ _____

STEP 1 / 2 / 3   OCTAL → DECIMAL

91

Convert 11000110 to the OCTAL equivalent.

7

① 12

② 2

35

$$10^0 = \underline{1}$$

63

① Expand

② Multiply

③ Add

91

$$\underbrace{11}_{3} \quad \underbrace{000}_{0} \quad \underbrace{110}_{6}$$

STEP 1   Example ▷   2)12
                                   ‾‾6‾‾ 0 (remainder)

Now we divide 2 into 6 and record the remainder.

                    2)12
                    2)6   0
                    ‾‾‾   ‾‾

Divide 2 into 6 and record the remainder (if any).

36

$$5^2 = 5 \times 5 = 25$$
$$5^1 = 5$$
$$5^0 = \underline{\qquad}$$

64

Convert 375 in the OCTAL system to a DECIMAL equivalent.

Expand 3 7 5 = $5(8^0) + 7(8^1) + 3(8^2)$

Multiply   = 5(1) + 7(8) + 3(64)

              = 5   + 56   + 192

Add   = _____

92

What is the DECIMAL equivalent of 11000110?

8

$2\overline{)\,12}$
$2\overline{)\,6}$ 0
  3   0

36

$$5^0 = \underline{1}$$

64

253

92

$$11000110 = 0(2^0) + 1(2^1) + 1(2^2) + 0(2^3) + 0(2^4) + 0(2^5)$$
$$+ 1(2^6) + 1(2^7)$$
$$= 0 + 2 + 4 + 0 + 0 + 0 + 64 + 128$$
$$= 198$$

STEP 1   Keep dividing the quotient and record the remainders.

$$2)\overline{12}$$
$$2)\overline{6} \quad 0$$
$$2)\overline{3} \quad 0$$

___ ___

$2^2 =$ _____ $=$ _____

$2^1 =$ _____

$2^0 =$ _____

What is the DECIMAL equivalent of 220 in the OCTAL system:

Expand $220 = 0(8^0) + 2(8^1) + 2(8^2)$

Multiply $=$ _____

Add $=$ _____

What is the BINARY equivalent of 438_{10}?

$$2 \overline{)12}$$
$$2 \overline{)6} \qquad 0$$
$$2 \overline{)3} \qquad 0$$
$$\qquad 1 \qquad 1$$

$$2^2 = \underline{2 \times 2} = \underline{4}$$
$$2^1 = \underline{2}$$
$$2^0 = \underline{1}$$

$$= 0 + 16 + 128$$
$$= 144$$

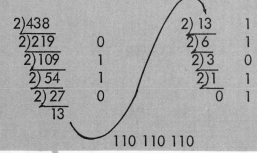

$$2 \overline{)438}$$ $$2 \overline{)13} \qquad 1$$
$$2 \overline{)219} \qquad 0$$ $$2 \overline{)6} \qquad 1$$
$$2 \overline{)109} \qquad 1$$ $$2 \overline{)3} \qquad 0$$
$$2 \overline{)54} \qquad 1$$ $$2 \overline{)1} \qquad 1$$
$$2 \overline{)27} \qquad 0$$ $$0 \qquad 1$$
$$\qquad 13$$

110 110 110

STEP 1   Divide the quotient (until 0) and record the remainder.

$$2\overline{)12}$$
$$2\overline{)6} \quad\quad 0$$
$$2\overline{)3} \quad\quad 0$$
$$2\overline{)1} \quad\quad 1$$

—— ——

Every numbering system is made of a specific number of different symbols.

(1)   The DECIMAL system is made of ___ different symbols.

(2)   The OCTAL system is made of ___ different symbols.

(3)   The BINARY system is made of ___ different symbols.

Convert 727 in the OCTAL system to its DECIMAL equivalent.

Expand   727 = _____

Multiply   = _____

Add   = _____

What is the OCTAL equivalent of 438_{10}?

```
2)12
 2)6    0
  2)3   0
   2)1  1
    0   1
```

① 10

② 8

③ 2

$$727 = 7(8^0) + 2(8^1) + 7(8^2)$$
$$= 7 \quad + 16 \quad + 448$$
$$= 471$$

```
8)438
 8)54   6
  8)6   6
   0    6

      666
```

STEP 1

2)12
2)6   0
2)3   0
2)1   1
   0   1

STEP 2: Sequence the remainders

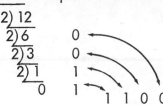

2)12
2)6   0
2)3   0
2)1   1
   0   1   1 1 0 0   ◁ This is your BI-
                        NARY number.

The BINARY equivalent of the DECIMAL number 12 is _____ .

Numbers larger than the number of different symbols (in any system) are made by combinations of the _____ .

Convert 535₈ to the DECIMAL equivalent.

What is the DECIMAL equivalent of 345₈ ?

1100

symbols

$$535_8 = 5(8^0) + 3(8^1) + 5(8^2)$$
$$= 5 \quad + 24 \quad + 320$$
$$= 349$$

$$345_8 = 5(8^0) + 4(8^1) + 3(8^2)$$
$$= 5 \quad + 32 \quad + 192$$
$$= 229$$

What is the BINARY equivalent of the DECIMAL 16?

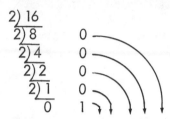

In the DECIMAL system, numbers larger than 9 are made of combinations of: 0, 1, 2, 3, 4, 5, 6, 7, 8, and 9.

For example, 685 is a combination of ___, ___, and ___.

CONVERSION BETWEEN SYSTEMS

> # **Binary to Octal**

GO TO NEXT FRAME

CONVERSION BETWEEN SYSTEMS

> # **Binary Coded Decimal**

GO TO NEXT FRAME

12

10000

40

6, 8, 5

68

96

46

What is the BINARY equivalent of the DECIMAL 19?

```
2) 19
   2) 9    1
      2) 4    1
         2) 2    0
            2) 1    0
               0    1
```

41

In the OCTAL system, numbers larger than 7 are made of combinations of: 0, 1, 2, 3, 4, 5, 6, and 7.

For example, 223 is a _____ of 2 and 3.

69

Converting from the BINARY system to the OCTAL system is very easy. We actually will change from the Base ____ to the Base ____.

97

The DECIMAL system has 10 different symbols. To indicate which symbol we want by lighting a bulb, we would need ____ different bulbs, one for each symbol.

13

10011

41

combination

69

2

8

97

10

What is the BINARY equivalent of the DECIMAL 24?

$$2\overline{)24}$$

In the BINARY system, numbers larger than 1 are made of combinations of 0 and 1.

For example, 10010 is a _____ of _____ and _____ .

$$1110011110_2$$

The above number is in the _____ system.

In order to reduce the number of bulbs or indicators to be used, a system called the BINARY CODED DECIMAL SYSTEM (BCD) was devised.

GO TO NEXT FRAME

```
2) 24
  2) 12      0
    2) 6     0
      2) 3   0
        2) 1   1
          0    1
```

11000

combination

1, 0

BINARY

15

What number in the BINARY system has the same value as 21 in the DECIMAL system?

43

Every symbol in any numbering system has a place value determined by its position. Positions start at the right with place 0.

In the number 5862

Place

etc. ◁ | 4 | 3 | 2 | 1 | 0 |

5 8 6 2

2 is in place 0
6 is in place 1
8 is in place 2
5 is in place ___ .

71

$\overline{1\ 1\ 1}$ $\overline{0\ 0\ 1}$ $\overline{1\ 1\ 0}$ ◁ start
3.2.1   3.2.1   3.2.1

To <u>convert</u> the above BINARY number into an OCTAL number, <u>divide</u> the BINARY number into groups of _____ symbols starting from the right.

(number)

99

The BINARY CODED DECIMAL (BCD) system uses only 4 indicators.

Using BCD, we can represent the _____ different Decimal symbols by using only 4 indicators of the _____ system.

15

```
2) 21
2) 10    1
  2) 5    0
   2) 2    1
    2) 1    0
      0    1
```
        10101

43

3

71

3

99

10

BCD

Convert 234 in the DECIMAL system to the equivalent number in the BINARY system?

44

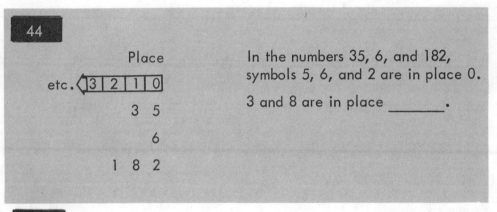

Place

etc. 3 2 1 0

3 5

6

1 8 2

In the numbers 35, 6, and 182, symbols 5, 6, and 2 are in place 0.

3 and 8 are in place _____.

72

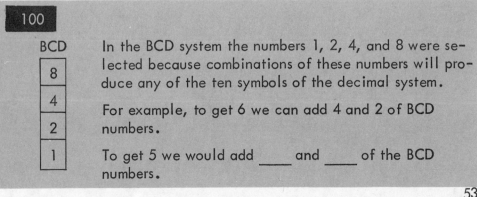

The above BINARY number was divided in groups of 3 starting from the (left, right).

100

BCD

| 8 |
| 4 |
| 2 |
| 1 |

In the BCD system the numbers 1, 2, 4, and 8 were selected because combinations of these numbers will produce any of the ten symbols of the decimal system.

For example, to get 6 we can add 4 and 2 of BCD numbers.

To get 5 we would add _____ and _____ of the BCD numbers.

```
2) 234              2) 14      1
  2) 117   0          2) 7      0
    2) 58   1           2) 3      1
      2) 29   0           2) 1      1
         14                 0      1
```

11101010

1

right

4

1

Decimal to Octal

GO TO NEXT FRAME

45

The DECIMAL value of any symbol of a different numbering system is:

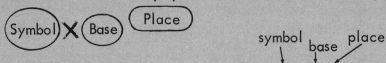

$(Symbol) \times (Base)^{(Place)}$

The symbol 3 of the number 35_{10} is equal to $3 \times 10^1 = 30$

The symbol 5 of the number 35_{10} is equal to $5 \times 10^0 =$ _____

73

<u>Divide</u> the following BINARY number in groups of three.

$$1\ 1\ 1\ 0\ 1\ 0\ 1\ 0\ 1 \quad \triangleleft \text{ start}$$

101

BCD		What BCD numbers would you add to get:
8	①	3: _____
4	②	7: _____
2	③	10: _____
1		

17

45

5

73

$$\underline{111}\ \underline{010}\ \underline{101}$$

101

① 2, 1

② 4, 2, 1

③ 8, 2

We will follow the same two steps when converting a DECIMAL number to an OCTAL number.

What is the base of the OCTAL NUMBERING SYSTEM?

The value of any number in the DECIMAL system is:

$$10^4 \quad 10^3 \quad 10^2 \quad 10^1 \quad 10^0$$
$$5 \quad\ \ 8 \quad\ \ 3 \quad\ \ 2 \quad\ \ 6$$

$$\left.\begin{array}{l} \\ \\ \end{array}\right\} \ \text{or}$$

6×10^0
2×10^1
3×10^2
$8 \times \underline{\quad}$
$5 \times \underline{\quad}$

To convert a BINARY number to an OCTAL number, the binary number is divided in groups of three.

Divide the following BINARY number in groups of three.

1 0 1 0 0 0 1 1

In a digital computer, the Binary system is used to represent the numbers that are selected.

A "1" is used to indicate a SELECTED number.

A "0" is used where a number is NOT SELECTED.

GO TO NEXT FRAME

8

$8 \times \underline{10^3}$

$5 \times \underline{10^4}$

$\underbrace{10}\ \underbrace{100}\ \underbrace{011}$

19

STEP 1   Divide the DECIMAL number by the base of the other
system.

$$8)\overline{24}$$

What is the DECIMAL number?

47

The DECIMAL value of any number in the BINARY system is:

$$
\begin{array}{ccccc}
2^4 & 2^3 & 2^2 & 2^1 & 2^0 \\
1 & 0 & 0 & 1 & 1
\end{array}
$$

$$
\begin{array}{l}
1 \times 2^0 \\
1 \times 2^1 \\
\text{or} \quad 0 \times 2^2 \\
0 \times 2^3 \\
1 \times \underline{}
\end{array}
$$

75

After a BINARY number is divided in groups of three, EACH GROUP
is converted to its decimal equivalent.

For example: 010   111   100   001
                 2   7   4   1

What are the DECIMAL equivalents of 110   111 ?

                                     ___   ___

103

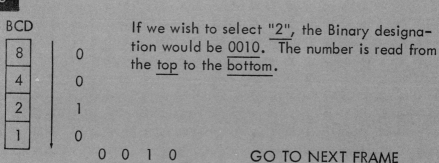

BCD

8	0
4	0
2	1
1	0

If we wish to select "2", the Binary designation would be 0010. The number is read from
the top to the bottom.

                    0   0   1   0

GO TO NEXT FRAME

19

24

47

$$1 \times 2^{\underline{4}}$$

75

$$\underbrace{110}_{\underline{6}} \quad \underbrace{111}_{\underline{7}}$$

103

STEP 1   Divide the DECIMAL number by the base of the other system and <u>record the remainders</u>.

$$8)\overline{24}$$
$$8)\overline{3} \quad \underline{}$$
$$0 \quad \underline{}$$

The DECIMAL values of symbols 100001110 are:

$2^8 \quad 2^7 \quad 2^6 \quad 2^5 \quad 2^4 \quad 2^3 \quad 2^2 \quad 2^1 \quad 2^0$

$1 \quad 0 \quad 0 \quad 0 \quad 0 \quad 1 \quad 1 \quad 1 \quad 0$ or

$$\left\{ \begin{array}{l} 0 \times 2^0 = 0 \\ 1 \times 2^1 = 2 \\ 1 \times 2^2 = 4 \\ 1 \times 2^3 = 8 \\ 0 \times 2^4 = 0 \\ 0 \times 2^5 = 0 \\ 0 \times 2^6 = 0 \\ 0 \times 2^7 = 0 \\ 1 \times 2^8 = 256 \end{array} \right\} \begin{array}{l} \text{in} \\ \text{DECIMAL} \\ \text{SYSTEM} \end{array}$$

GO TO NEXT FRAME

Divide this BINARY number in groups of three and <u>write</u> the DECIMAL equivalent.

1 0 1 0 1 1 1 1 1 0 0 0

Write the Binary designation if we wish to select "4".

8	__
4	__
2	__
1	__

$$\begin{array}{r} 8\overline{)\,24} \\ 8\overline{)\,3} \quad 0 \\ \overline{0} \quad 3 \end{array}$$

$$\underbrace{101}_{5} \quad \underbrace{011}_{3} \quad \underbrace{111}_{7} \quad \underbrace{000}_{0}$$

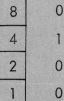

8	0
4	1
2	0
1	0

STEP 2. Sequence the remainders.

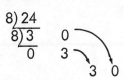

What is the OCTAL equivalent of the DECIMAL 24?

The DECIMAL values of each of the BINARY symbols is illustrated below:

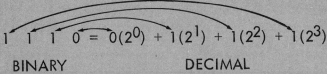

BINARY   DECIMAL

GO TO NEXT FRAME

Divide this BINARY number in groups of three and <u>write</u> the DECIMAL equivalent.

    1 0 1 1 1 0 1 0

If we wish to select "6" the Binary designation would be 0110.

8	0 or
4	1
2	1
1	0

What would be the Binary designation for 3?

8	__
4	__
2	__
1	__

30

$$\underbrace{10}_{2} \ \underbrace{111}_{7} \ \underbrace{010}_{2}$$

8	0
4	0
2	1
1	1

What is the OCTAL equivalent of the DECIMAL 385?

To convert a BINARY number to its DECIMAL equivalent, THREE steps are performed.

STEP 1 is: _____.

STEP 1 2 3 · BINARY → DECIMAL Expand

◁ Start
101 011 111 000 ----- BINARY number
‿‿‿ ‿‿‿ ‿‿‿ ‿‿‿ --- Divide into groups of three
  5   3   7   0 --- DECIMAL equivalent of each group

To convert the BINARY number 101011111000 into the OCTAL equivalent, the above steps were performed. THE NUMBER 5370 IS THE
OCTAL EQUIVALENT OF THE BINARY NUMBER 101011111000.

GO TO NEXT FRAME

What would be the Binary designation for 7?

| 8 |
| 4 |
| 2 |
| 1 |

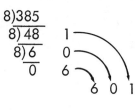

601

Expand

8	0
4	1
2	1
1	1

23

What number in the OCTAL SYSTEM has the same value as 934 in the DECIMAL system?

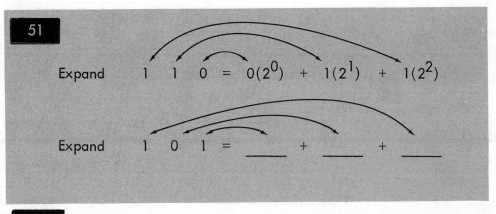

51

Expand   1   1   0   = $0(2^0)$ + $1(2^1)$ + $1(2^2)$

Expand   1   0   1   =   ____   +   ____   +   ____

79

Let us find the <u>OCTAL equivalent</u> of the BINARY NUMBER
1 1 0 0 0 1.

First, starting from the right, divide the number in groups of three.

107

On the IBM Punched Card used as inputs to the 1401 computer, rows A, B and C are added to provide additional inputs.

C
B
A
8
4
2
1

GO TO NEXT FRAME

```
8) 934
  8) 116    6
    8) 14    4
      8) 1    6
        0    1
```

1646

$$101 = \underline{1(2^0)} + \underline{0(2^1)} + \underline{1(2^2)}$$

$$\underset{\smile}{110} \quad \underset{\smile}{001}$$

What number in the BINARY system is equivalent to 73 in the
DECIMAL system?

52

Expand $1001 = 1(2^0) + 0(2^1) + 0(2^2) + 1(2^3)$

Expand $1100 = $ _____ + _____ + _____ + _____

80

110 001

Write the decimal equivalent of each group.

108

What would be the Binary designation for A9?

C
B
A
8
4
2
1

$$2\overline{)73}$$
$$2\overline{)36} \quad 1$$
$$2\overline{)18} \quad 0$$
$$2\overline{)9} \quad 0$$
$$2\overline{)4} \quad 1$$
$$2\overline{)2} \quad 0$$
$$2\overline{)1} \quad 0$$
$$0 \quad 1$$

1001001

52

$$1100 = \underline{0(2^0)} + \underline{0(2^1)} + \underline{1(2^2)} + \underline{1(2^3)}$$

80

$$\underbrace{110}_{6} \quad \underbrace{001}_{1}$$

108

C	0
B	0
A	1
8	1
4	0
2	0
1	1

To convert a number from the DECIMAL system to a numbering system
with a smaller Base;

STEP 1. Divide _____ number by _____ of system
with smaller base and record all remainders.

STEP 2. Sequence _____.

53

To convert a BINARY number to its DECIMAL equivalent, THREE
steps are performed.

STEP 1 is Expand

STEP 2 is _____

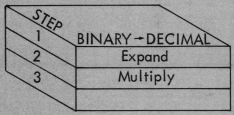

STEP	BINARY → DECIMAL
1	
2	Expand
3	Multiply

81

$$110 \quad 001$$
$$\underbrace{} \quad \underbrace{}$$
$$6 \qquad 1$$

What is the OCTAL equivalent of the above BINARY number
(110001)?

---

109   Write the Binary designations for the following:

B1
C
B
A
8
4
2
1

B6
C
B
A
8
4
2
1

AB4
C
B
A
8
4
2
1

25

DECIMAL, Base
Remainders

53

Multiply

81

61

109

	B1				B6				AB4		
		C	0			C	0			C	0
		B	1			B	1			B	1
		A	0			A	0			A	1
		8	0			8	0			8	0
		4	0			4	1			4	1
		2	0			2	1			2	0
		1	1			1	0			1	0

STEP 1. _____ and _____ remainders.

STEP 2. _____ remainders.

54

$$\underline{\text{Expand}} \ 1001 = 1(2^0) + 0(2^1) + 0(2^2) + 1(2^3)$$

$$\underline{\text{Multiply}} \quad = 1(1) \ + 0(2) \ + 0(4) \ + 1(8)$$

$$= 1 \quad\ \ + 0 \quad\ \ + 0 \quad\ \ + 8$$

GO TO NEXT FRAME

82

What is the OCTAL equivalent of the following BINARY number?

100001110

110

What is the COMPUTER designation for the
Binary number 0011001?

C	0
B	0
A	1
8	1
4	0
2	0
1	1

_____

26

Divide, record

Sequence

54

82

$$\underbrace{100}_{4} \quad \underbrace{001}_{1} \quad \underbrace{110}_{6}$$

416

110

A9

Binary to Decimal

GO TO NEXT FRAME

55

$\underline{\text{Expand}}$ $110 = 0(2^0) + 1(2^1) + 1(2^2)$

$\underline{\text{Multiply}}$ $= 0(1) \quad + 1(2) \quad + 1(4)$

$= \underline{\hspace{1cm}} + \underline{\hspace{1cm}} + \underline{\hspace{1cm}}$

83

$\underline{\text{Convert}}$ the following BINARY number into an OCTAL number

10111001010100

111

Write the COMPUTER equivalent of the following Binary numbers in the BCD system.

   (1.)   0100010   (3.)   0110010

   (2.)   0011000   (4.)   0000001

27

55

$= \underline{0} + \underline{2} + \underline{4}$

83

$$\underbrace{10}_{2} \quad \underbrace{111}_{7} \quad \underbrace{001}_{1} \quad \underbrace{010}_{2} \quad \underbrace{100}_{4}$$

27124

111

① B2

② A8

③ AB2

④ 1

28

Before we convert numbers in the BINARY system to numbers in the DECIMAL system, we will review a little basic mathematics which is necessary for this conversion.

GO TO NEXT FRAME

56

To convert a BINARY number to its DECIMAL equivalent, THREE steps are performed.

STEP 1 is Expand.

STEP 2 is Multiply.

STEP 3 is _____ .

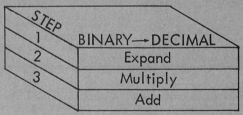

STEP	BINARY→DECIMAL
1	Expand
2	Multiply
3	Add

84   CONVERSION BETWEEN SYSTEMS

Octal to Binary

GO TO NEXT FRAME

112   You have just learned the numbering systems most commonly used with digital computers. They are:

1. DECIMAL   Base 10
2. OCTAL   Base 8
3. BINARY   Base 2
4. BINARY CODED
      DECIMAL (BCD) ————→

8
4
2
1

GO TO NEXT FRAME

28

56

Add

84

112

GO TO FRAME 29 ON PAGE 23

GO TO FRAME 57 ON PAGE 23

GO TO FRAME 85 ON PAGE 23

GO TO CHAPTER III ON NEXT PAGE

NOTES

Chapter III Binary Arithmetic

A digital computer performs arithmetic functions in the binary system. To fully understand computer operation and programing, a knowledge of binary arithmetic is necessary. Chapter III teaches the student how to add, subtract, multiply and divide in the binary system.

Chapter Outline

III Binary Arithmetic
1. Binary Addition
2. Binary Subtraction
3. Binary Multiplication
4. Binary Division

NOW, TURN THE PAGE AND READ FRAME 1 OF CHAPTER III.

NOTES

Binary Addition

GO TO NEXT FRAME

To Add three (3) or more numbers, we add the first two (2) numbers and get partial answer 1.

Then, we add the next number to partial answer 1 and get partial answer 2.

This continues until all numbers are added.

GO TO NEXT FRAME

Problem→Subt. Col. 1→Subt. Col. 2→Subt. Col. 3 ←We do not have

to borrow be-
cause we are not
subtracting a
larger number
from a smaller
number.

```
                    Borrow
              Borrow     10          10
              0  10    0  0  10    0  0  10
1110      1 1 (1) 0   1 (1) 1 0   1 1 1 0
- 11      -    1  1   -   1  1   -   1  1
              1         1  1         1  1
```

Subtract Col. 3

Circle the product in each of the following:

(a)	(b)	(c)
32	111	100
× 3	× 10	× 111
96	1110	11100

41

81

0

121

(a)

32
× 3
(96)

(b)

111
× 10
(1110)

(c)

100
× 111
(11100)

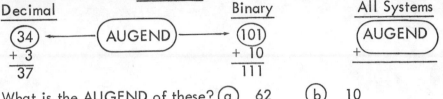

2	In all numbering systems, the number we are ADDING TO is called the <u>AUGEND</u>.

Decimal		Binary	All Systems

$\text{(34)} \leftarrow \boxed{\text{AUGEND}} \rightarrow \text{(101)} \qquad \boxed{\text{AUGEND}}$

$$\begin{array}{r} \text{(34)} \\ +\ 3 \\ \hline 37 \end{array} \qquad \begin{array}{r} \text{(101)} \\ +\ 10 \\ \hline 111 \end{array} \qquad \begin{array}{r} \\ + \\ \hline \end{array}$$

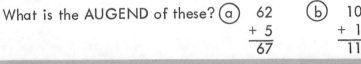

What is the AUGEND of these? (a) $\begin{array}{r} 62 \\ +\ 5 \\ \hline 67 \end{array}$ (b) $\begin{array}{r} 10 \\ +\ 1 \\ \hline 11 \end{array}$

42

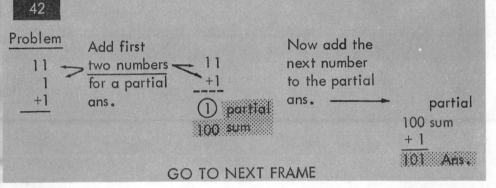

<u>Problem</u>

$$\begin{array}{r} 11 \\ 1 \\ +1 \\ \hline \end{array}$$

Add first two numbers for a partial ans.

$$\begin{array}{r} 11 \\ +1 \\ \hline \end{array}$$

① partial
100 sum

Now add the next number to the partial ans. ⟶

partial
100 sum
+ 1
―――
101 Ans.

GO TO NEXT FRAME

82

Problem→Subt. Col. 1→Subt. Col. 2→Subt. Col. 3→Subt. Col. 4

$$\begin{array}{r} 1110 \\ -\ 11 \\ \hline \end{array}$$

Borrow

$$\begin{array}{r} 0\ \ 10 \\ 1\ 1\ \cancel{1}\ \cancel{0} \\ -\ \ \ 1\ \ 1 \\ \hline 1 \end{array}$$

Borrow

$$\begin{array}{r} 10 \\ 0\ \cancel{0}\ 10 \\ 1\ \cancel{1}\ \cancel{1}\ \cancel{0} \\ -\ \ \ 1\ \ 1 \\ \hline 1\ \ 1 \end{array}$$

$$\begin{array}{r} 10 \\ 0\ \cancel{0}\ 10 \\ 1\ \cancel{1}\ \cancel{1}\ \cancel{0} \\ -\ \ \ 1\ \ 1 \\ \hline 0\ \ 1\ \ 1 \end{array}$$

$$\begin{array}{r} 10 \\ 0\ \cancel{0}\ 10 \\ 1\ \cancel{1}\ \cancel{1}\ \cancel{0} \\ -\ \ \ 1\ \ 1 \\ \hline 0\ \ 1\ \ 1 \end{array}$$

Subtract Col. 4

122

In all numbering systems;

the number we are <u>multiplying</u> is called the _____ ;

the number we are <u>multiplying by</u> is called the _____ ;

the <u>answer</u> is called the _____ .

2

    (a) 62

    (b) 10

42

82

1

122

multiplicand

multiplier

product

3

      a.   b.

    261   100
   + 4   + 10
   265   110

n the above examples, 261 and 100 are called the _____.

43

Because we will frequently add three ones (1), let us solve this:

Problem	Step 1	Step 2
1 ⟶ 1		
1 ⟶ +1		
+1	10 partial sum	10 partial sum
		+1
		___ What is the Ans.?

83

Solve

    1 1 0 1

  −   1 1 0

123

Fill in the blanks with the words: Product, Multiplicand, Multiplier

       _____

  × _____

     _____

     _____

3

augend

43

11

83

```
      10
  0   Ø  10
  X̸   X̸  Ø   1
−     1   1   0
      1   1   1
```

123

Multiplicand

× Multiplier

Product

Circle the augend in each of the following:

(a)	(b)	(c)
826	1100	1001
+ 53	+ 10	+110
879	1110	1111

BINARY Addition

$$0 + 0 = \underline{\hphantom{xxx}}$$
$$1 + 0 = \underline{\hphantom{xxx}}$$
$$0 + 1 = \underline{\hphantom{xxx}}$$
$$1 + 1 = \underline{\hphantom{xxx}}$$
$$1 + 1 + 1 = \underline{\hphantom{xxx}}$$

Solve

```
1 1 0 1 0 0
-       1 1 1
```

BINARY MULTIPLICATION is the same as Decimal Multiplication

DECIMAL	BINARY
24	101
× 2	× 1
48 ← 2 × 24 = 48	101 ← 101 × 1 = 101

Multiply the following:

1	0	11	11
×0	×1	× 0	× 1

89

4

ⓐ
(826)
+ 53
―――
879

ⓑ
(1100)
+ 10
―――
1110

ⓒ
(1001)
+110
―――
1111

44

0
1
1
10
11

84

1 0 1 1 0 1

124

1
×0
――
0

0
×1
――
0

11
× 0
――
00

11
× 1
――
11

90

5	Also, in all numbering systems, the number we are <u>ADDING</u> is called the <u>ADDEND</u>.

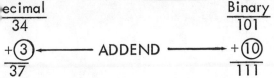

Decimal		Binary	All Systems
34		101	AUGEND
+③ ◄—— ADDEND ——►		+⑩	+(ADDEND)
37		111	

What is the ADDEND of these? ⓐ 62 ⓑ 10
                                      + 5   + 1
                                       67   11

45

Problem	Step 1	Step 2
111	‾1‾ ‾1‾ ‾1‾	
111	+1 1 1	
110	① ① ①	
	1 1 1 0 partial sum	1 1 1 0 partial sum
		+1 1 0
	What is the Answer? _____	

85

There is another way to subtract <u>BINARY NUMBERS</u>. It is called

SUBTRACTION through COMPLEMENTING

GO TO NEXT FRAME

125	In BINARY MULTIPLICATION, when you multiply:

NUMBER ⟶ 10   NUMBER ⟶ 10
  × 0   × 0   × 1   × 1
   0   0   NUMBER ⟶ 10

Multiply the following: ⓐ 111   ⓑ 111   ⓒ 101   ⓓ 101
                              × 0   × 1   × 0   × 1

| 5 |

(a) 5
(b) 1

| 45 |

1 0 1 0 0

| 85 |

| 125 |

(a) 111
× 0
—
0

(b) 111
× 1
—
111

(c) 101
× 0
—
0

(d) 101
× 1
—
101

```
 261              100
+  4             + 10
─────            ─────
 265              110
```

In the above examples, 4 and 10 are called the _____ .

Add the following:

(a) 110   (b) 110
      11   11
      10   101
     ───   ───

First we will learn How to Complement a Number.

There are two steps in complementing.

STEP I. Starting from the right side of the number   10 ┊ 100
         rewrite all numbers through the first one (1).   ┊ 100

STEP II. Invert all numbers to the left of the first   01 ┊
         one (1).   ┊

GO TO NEXT FRAME

BINARY MULTIPLICATION with two or more numbers is also the same as Decimal Multiplication.

DECIMAL   BINARY
─────────   ────────
       24   101
     ×12   ×11
     ─────   ─────
       48←—2×24 = 48   101←—1×101 = 101
Add in 24←—1×24 = 24   Add in 101←—1×101 = 101
Decimal–288   Binary–1111

Multiply the following: (a) 10   (b) 10   (c) 100
                             ×10   ×11   ×11

addend

46

(a) 1011

(b) 1110

86

126

(a)
```
   10
 × 10
 ────
   00
  10
 ────
  100
```

(b)
```
   10
 × 11
 ────
   10
  10
 ────
  110
```

(c)
```
  100
 × 11
 ────
  100
 100
 ────
 1100
```

94

7

Circle the underline addend in each of the following:

ⓐ	ⓑ	ⓒ
826	1100	1001
+ 53	+ 10	+110
879	1110	1111

47

Add the following:

ⓐ   11001
       101
      1001

ⓑ   1000110
      1100101
       111100

87   COMPLEMENTING

STEP I: Starting from the right side of the number, rewrite all numbers through the first one (1).

1100100	10110	1010000
Step I ⟶ 100	10	10000

Write Step I of 100111000

127

Multiply the following:

ⓐ	ⓑ	ⓒ
111	101	101
× 10	× 11	× 10

ⓐ
826
+㊳
―――
879

ⓑ
1100
+ ⑩
―――
1110

ⓒ
1001
+ ⑩
―――
1111

ⓐ 100111

ⓑ 11100111

1000

ⓐ
111
× 10
―――
000
111
―――
1110

ⓑ
101
× 11
―――
101
101
―――
1111

ⓒ
101
× 10
―――
000
101
―――
1010

In <u>all</u> numbering systems:

the number we are <u>adding to</u> is called the _____ ,

and the number we are <u>adding</u> is called the _____ .

48

Add the following:

  ⓐ 10   ⓑ 1101
     11   1010
     10   10
     <u>11</u>   <u>101</u>

88

<u>Write Step I of the following:</u>

  1110001110   110001   1000   11100

128

If the multiplier has three or more ones (1), the adding part of Multiplication will have to be done adding the first two numbers and getting a <u>Partial Solution</u>. Then add the third number to this partial solution. The next frame will show this.

GO TO NEXT FRAME

8

augend

addend

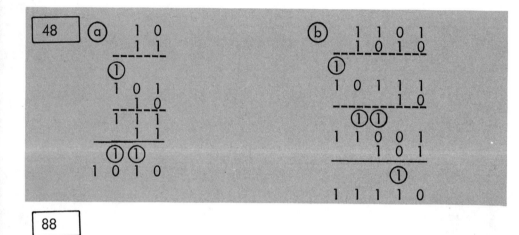

48

88

10   1   1000   100

128

9 The <u>ANSWER</u> to an addition problem (in all numbering systems) is called the <u>SUM</u>.

Decimal	Binary	All Systems
34	101	AUGEND
+ 3	+ 10	+ ADDEND
(37) ◄——— SUM ———► (111)		(SUM)

What is the SUM of these? (a) 62
  + 5
  ——
  67

(b) 10
  + 1
  ——
  11

---

49 We have just learned how to add BINARY numbers.
Now . . .

Binary Subtraction

GO TO NEXT FRAME

---

89 STEP I: Rewrite all numbers through the first one (1).
<u>STEP II</u>: Invert all remaining numbers to the left of the first one (1).

To invert we <u>change</u> $\begin{cases} 0 \text{ to } 1 \\ 1 \text{ to } 0 \end{cases}$

Therefore: 111 000 101
Inverted: 000 111 010
<u>Only invert the following:</u> 110110
  10110
  01000

---

129 Multiply the following:

Problem	Multiply	Add
111	111	111
×111	×111	×111
	111 ————►	111
	111 ————►	111
	111	10101 partial sum
		111
		110001 Ans.

GO TO NEXT FRAME

9

(a) 67

(b) 11

49

89

001001
01001
10111

129

```
   261            100
 +   4          + 10
 -----          -----
   265            110
```

In the above examples, 265 and 110 are called the _____.

In all numbering systems, the number we are SUBTRACTING
FROM is called the MINUEND.

Decimal   Binary   All Systems

(34) ◄———— MINUEND ————► (110)   (MINUEND)

```
  - 2                                - 10
  ----                               ----
   32                                 100
```

What is the MINUEND of these?   (a) 27   (b) 11
                                     - 5   - 1
                                     ----   ----
                                      22   10

Complementing

STEP I: Rewrite all numbers through the first one (1).
STEP II: Invert all remaining numbers to the left of the first one (1).

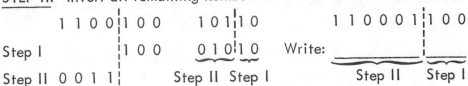

```
          1 1 0 0 | 1 0 0      1 0 1 | 1 0        1 1 0 0 0 1 | 1 0 0

Step I           | 1 0 0      0 1 0 | 1 0   Write: _____ | ____

Step II  0 0 1 1 |            Step II Step I        Step II    Step I
```

Multiply the following:

```
     1011
   x  111
```

SUM

ⓐ 27

ⓑ 11

0 0 1 1 1 0 1 0 0

```
      1011
    × 111
    ─────
     1011
    1011
    ──────
  100001    partial sum
   1011
  ───────
  1001101  Ans.
```

Circle the <u>sum</u> in each of the following:

(a)	(b)	(c)
826	1100	1001
+ 53	+ 10	+110
879	1110	1111

78	111
−11	− 10
67	101

In the above examples, 78 and 111 are called the _____.

Complement the following:

(a) 1010

(b) 10001

(c) 101110100

Multiply the following:

    1101
  × 101

11

ⓐ
826
+ 53
(879)

ⓑ
1100
+ 10
(1110)

ⓒ
1001
+110
(1111)

51

minuend

91

ⓐ 0110

ⓑ 01111

ⓒ 010001100

131

The multiplier has <u>only two ones</u> (1).

```
   1101
 × 101
   1101
  0000
 1101
1000001
```

In all numbering systems:

The number we are <u>adding to</u> is called the _____ ;

the number we are <u>adding</u> is called the _____ ;

the <u>answer</u> is called the _____ .

Circle the <u>minuend</u> in each of the following:

ⓐ	ⓑ	ⓒ
55	1001	1110
− 4	− 1	−100
51	1000	1010

<u>Complement</u> the following:

ⓐ   1100010

ⓑ   1000

ⓒ   11

<u>Multiply</u> the following:

$$\begin{array}{r} 1001 \\ \times\ 1111 \end{array}$$

augend

addend

sum

52

(a)
(55)
$\frac{- 4}{51}$

(b)
(1001)
$\frac{- 1}{1000}$

(c)
(1110)
$\frac{-100}{1010}$

92

(a) 0011110

(b) 1000

(c) 01

132

$$
\begin{array}{r}
1001 \\
\times 1111 \\
\hline
1001 \\
1001 \\
\hline
\end{array}
$$

11011   partial sum 1

1001

111111   partial sum 2

1001

$\overline{10000111}$ Ans.

13

Fill in the blanks with the words: Sum, Augend, Addend

$$+ \frac{\underline{\qquad}}{\underline{\qquad}}$$

_____

53   The number we are SUBTRACTING (in all numbering systems) is called the SUBTRAHEND.

Decimal	Binary	All Systems
34	110	MINUEND
-② ⟵ Subtrahend ⟶	-⑩	-(SUBTRAHEND)

What is the SUBTRAHEND of these?   ⓐ 27   ⓑ 11
                                        - 5   - 1
                                        ‾‾22‾‾   ‾‾10‾‾

93

Now that we have learned to complement a number, let us see how to

SUBTRACT through Complementing

GO TO NEXT FRAME

133

Multiply the following:

        1101
      × 1111

13

augend
+ addend
─────────
sum

53

    (a) 5
    (b) 1

93

133

```
        1101
      × 1111
      ─────
        1101
       1101
      ───────
      100111    partial sum 1
       1101
      ───────
      1011011   partial sum 2
      1101
    ─────────
    11000011  Ans.
```

14

The BINARY SYSTEM consists of <u>two</u> numbers. What are they?

54

```
 78          111
-11         - 10
───         ────
 67          101
```

In the above examples, 11 and 10 are called the _____.

94 To SUBTRACT through complementing, we perform three (3) operations:

(1) COMPLEMENT the number we are subtracting (subtrahend)

(2) ADD the complement <u>to</u> the number we are subtracting FROM (Minuend)

(3) ELIMINATE numbers (in answer) beyond the number of digits in the number being subtracted FROM.

GO TO NEXT FRAME

134 We have learned BINARY Addition, Subtraction and Multiplication. We will now learn:

Binary Division

GO TO NEXT FRAME

14

0, 1

54

subtrahend

94

134

15

There are only FOUR combinations in which two numbers can be added.

$$\begin{array}{cccc} 0 & 1 & 0 & 1 \\ +0 & +0 & +1 & +1 \\ \hline \end{array}$$

GO TO NEXT FRAME

55.

Circle the subtrahend in each of the following:

ⓐ

$$\begin{array}{r} 55 \\ -4 \\ \hline 51 \end{array}$$

ⓑ

$$\begin{array}{r} 1001 \\ -\quad 1 \\ \hline 1000 \end{array}$$

ⓒ

$$\begin{array}{r} 1110 \\ -100 \\ \hline 1010 \end{array}$$

95   SUBTRACTION through COMPLEMENTING

Problem

1100 ◄— From (Minuend)
- 1010 ◄— Subtracting (Subtrahend)

① COMPLEMENT the subtrahend

   1. The subtrahend is Always on the _____ (bottom, top).

   2. Write the subtrahend.

135   In all numbering systems, the number we are DIVIDING is called the DIVIDEND.

Decimal	Binary	All Systems

$12\overline{)②④}$ ◄—— DIVIDEND —— $10\overline{)①①⓪}$ with 11 above, $\overline{)\text{DIVIDEND}}$

What is the DIVIDEND of these? ⓐ $12\overline{)48}$ with 4 above   ⓑ $11\overline{)110}$ with 10 above

111

55

ⓐ

55

−④

51

ⓑ

1001

− ①

1000

ⓒ

1110

−⑩⓪

1010

95

bottom

1010

135

ⓐ 48

ⓑ 110

16 The FOUR combinations may be written <u>two</u> different equivalent ways

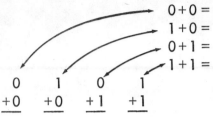

$$0+0 =$$
$$1+0 =$$
$$0+1 =$$
$$1+1 =$$

0	1	0	1
+0	+0	+1	+1

GO TO NEXT FRAME

56

In <u>all</u> numbering systems:

the number we are <u>subtracting from</u> is called the _____, and

the number we are <u>subtracting</u> is called the _____.

96   SUBTRACTION through COMPLEMENTING

Problem

  1100
− 1010

① COMPLEMENT the subtrahend

  1 0 1 0

Step II Step I

Complement this number.

136

$$5\overline{)10}\;\;\;^2 \qquad 110\overline{)11110}\;\;\;^{101}$$

In the above examples, 10 and 11110 are called the _____.

16

56

minuend
subtrahend

96

0 1 1 0

136

dividend

Solve the remaining two problems in the DECIMAL system.

$$0+0 = 0$$
$$1+0 = 1$$
$$0+1 = \underline{}$$
$$1+1 = \underline{}$$

57 In <u>all</u> numbering systems, the <u>ANSWER</u> is called the DIFFERENCE.

Decimal	Binary	All Systems
34	110	MINUEND
− 2	− 10	− SUBTRAHEND
(32) ←——— DIFFERENCE ———→ (100)		(DIFFERENCE)

What is the DIFFERENCE of these?

(a)
```
  27
-  5
  22
```

(b)
```
  11
-  1
  10
```

97 <u>SUBTRACTION through COMPLEMENTING</u>

<u>Problem</u>

```
 1100
-1010
```
→ subtrahend ——→

① COMPLEMENT the subtrahend

1 0 1 0 ——→ 0110 complement

Step II Step 1

② ADD complement <u>TO</u> minuend

Add these.
```
 1100
+0110
```

137

Circle the <u>dividend</u> in each of the following:

(a)
```
    7
7)49
```

(b)
```
   10
10)100
```

(c)
```
     100
111)11100
```

17

1
2

57

ⓐ 22
ⓑ 10

97

10010

137

a   b   c

$$7\overline{)49}$$ $$10\overline{)100}$$ $$111\overline{)11100}$$

with quotients 7, 10, and 100 respectively

18

ADDING combinations of "0" and "1" in the binary system is very similar to that of the decimal system.

Decimal	Binary
$0+0 = 0$	$0+0 = 0$

Adding $0+0$ in the binary system is the _____ as in the decimal system.

58

$$\begin{array}{r} 78 \\ -\ 11 \\ \hline 67 \end{array} \qquad\qquad \begin{array}{r} 111 \\ -\ 10 \\ \hline 101 \end{array}$$

In the above examples, 67 and 101 are called the _____.

---

98   SUBTRACTION through COMPLEMENTING

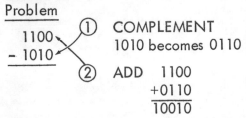

Problem

$$\begin{array}{r} 1100 \\ -\ 1010 \\ \hline \end{array}$$

① COMPLEMENT
1010 becomes 0110

② ADD   1100
        +0110
        ‾‾‾‾‾
        10010

③ ELIMINATE number of digits beyond minuend

$$\begin{array}{r} 1100 \\ +\ 0110 \\ \hline 1\ 0010 \end{array}$$

In this case, are there any numbers to be ELIMINATED? If so, what are they?

---

138   In all numbering systems, the number we are DIVIDING BY is called the DIVISOR.

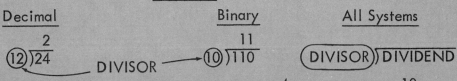

Decimal	Binary	All Systems
$\begin{array}{r}2\\ 12\overline{)24}\end{array}$	$\begin{array}{r}11\\ 10\overline{)110}\end{array}$	(DIVISOR) DIVIDEND

DIVISOR

What is the divisor of these?   ⓐ $\begin{array}{r}4\\ 12\overline{)48}\end{array}$ ⓑ $\begin{array}{r}10\\ 11\overline{)110}\end{array}$

117

same

difference

yes

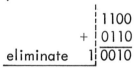

```
            ¦ 1100
        +  ¦ 0110
eliminate  1¦ 0010
```

ⓐ 12

ⓑ 11

Decimal	Binary
$0 + 0 = 0$	$0 + 0 = 0$
$1 + 0 = 1$	$1 + 0 = 1$
$0 + 1 = 1$	$0 + 1 = 1$

Write the THREE adding combinations of "0" and "1" in the binary system that give the same answer as in the decimal system.

59

Circle the difference in each of the following:

ⓐ

```
  55
-  4
  51
```

ⓑ

```
1001
-   1
1000
```

ⓒ

```
 1110
 -100
 1010
```

99

1. The MINUEND has 4 digits.

2. The Ans. has 5 digits.

3. Therefore, ELIMINATE the 5th digit.

```
         1100  minuend
       + 0110
eliminate 1 0010  Ans.
```

4. The correct ANSWER to the problem becomes 0010 or 10.

GO TO NEXT FRAME

139

```
      2
   5) 10
```

```
        101
   110) 11110
```

In the above examples, 5 and 110 are called the _____.

119

19

0 + 0

1 + 0

0 + 1

59

 (a)

55
– 4
⸰51⸰

(b)

1001
– 1
⸰1000⸰

(c)

1110
–100
⸰1010⸰

99

139

divisor

he adding combinations of "0+0", "1+0", and "0+1" result in the
ame answer in both the binary and decimal systems because in these
ystems both _____ and _____ are equivalent.

60

n all numbering systems:

he number we are <u>subtracting from</u> is called the _____ ;

he number we are <u>subtracting</u> is called the _____ ;

he <u>answer</u> is called the _____ .

100   Let us try another problem.

roblem   1. COMPLEMENT: 100100 becomes 011100

111001   / 2. ADD: ┆111001
100100 ╱   + ┆011100
_____   1┆010101

            3. ELIMINATE:

Vhat is your Answer?

140

Circle the divisor in each of the following:

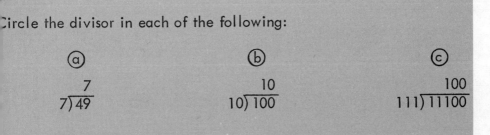

      ⓐ   ⓑ   ⓒ

$$7 \overline{)49}$$ with 7 above $$10 \overline{)100}$$ with 10 above $$111 \overline{)11100}$$ with 100 above

0

1

minuend

subtrahend

difference

0 1 0 1 0 1

or

a zero in front
of any number
can be dropped

0 1 0 1 0 1

ⓐ

$$7 \overline{)49} \quad 7$$

ⓑ

$$10 \overline{)100} \quad 10$$

ⓒ

$$111 \overline{)11100} \quad 100$$

the decimal system:

$1 + 1 = 2$

the number "2" a number in the binary system?

ill in the blanks with the words: Difference, Minuend, Subtrahend

_____

−   _____

_____

zero in front of any number in any numbering system can be <u>added</u>
r dropped without changing the value of the number.

| <u>DECIMAL</u> | $038 = 38 = 0038$ |
| <u>BINARY</u> | $010 = 10 = 0010$ |

GO TO NEXT FRAME

n all numbering systems, the number we are <u>dividing</u> is called the
_____ and the number we <u>divide by</u> is called the _____.

21

no

61

Minuend

− Subtrahend

Difference

101

141

dividend

divisor

"2" is not in the binary system.

However, because the answer to $1+1$ in the decimal system is "2", the answer to $1+1$ in the binary system must be equivalent to _____ .

---

62 Binary subtraction is very similar to decimal subtraction:

Decimal	Binary
$0-0=0$	$0-0=0$
$1-0=1$	$1-0=1$
$1-1=0$	$1-1=0$
②$-1=1$ ── equivalent ── ⑩$-1=1$	

GO TO NEXT FRAME

102

Always add zeros (if necessary) in front of subtrahend to fill same number of columns as the minuend.

$$\begin{array}{r} 1\,1\,0\,0 \\ -\quad 1\,0 \end{array} \xrightarrow{\text{becomes}} \begin{array}{r} 1\,1\,0\,0 \\ -\,0\,0\,1\,0 \end{array}$$

What does $\begin{array}{r} 101100 \\ -\quad 110 \end{array}$ become?

---

142 In all numbering systems, the ANSWER to a division problem is called the QUOTIENT.

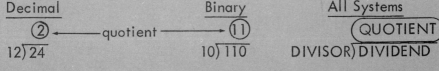

Decimal	Binary	All Systems
② ←── quotient ──→ ⑪		(QUOTIENT)
12)24	10)110	DIVISOR)DIVIDEND

What is the quotient of these?   (a) $12\overline{)48}$ quotient 4   (b) $11\overline{)110}$ quotient 10

22

2

62

102

```
  101100
- 000110
```

142

ⓐ   4

ⓑ   10

Convert "2" in the decimal system to its <u>EQUIVALENT</u> in the binary system.

63

Decimal	Binary	Any number (in all numbering systems) subtracted from itself = 0
0 - 0 = 0	0 - 0 = 0	
1 - 0 = 1	1 - 0 = 1	Decimal: 2 - 2 = 0
1 - 1 = 0	1 - 1 = 0	8 - 8 = 0
2 - 1 = 1	10 - 1 = 1	Binary: 1 - 1 = 0
		10 - 10 = ____

103

① COMPLEMENT

Problem

  11001
− 01100

01100 —— complement ——→ 10100

② ADD

  11001
+ 10100
 101101

③ Eliminate

What is your answer?

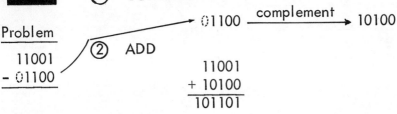

143

$$\frac{2}{5)\overline{10}} \qquad \frac{101}{110)\overline{11110}}$$

In the above examples, 2 and 101 are called the _____.

23

10

63

0

103

01101

or

1101

143

quotient

"2" in the decimal system is _____ to _____ in the
binary system.

Binary   Solve the following

0 - 0 = 0   1 1 0 1   1 0 1 1
1 - 0 = 1   - 1 0 0   - 1 0 0 1
1 - 1 = 0
10 - 1 = 1
(10 - 10 = 0)

		10001
Problem	Add Zeros	- 00110

Problem

10001   1   Complement
- 110   00110 ——————→ 11010

             2   Add

             3   Eliminate

What is your Answer?

Circle the quotient in each of the following:

ⓐ   ⓑ   ©

   7   10   100
7) 49   10) 100   111) 11100

equivalent

10

1001

0010

```
  ┆ 10001
 +┆ 11010    Add
1 ┆ 01011
  ┆
 1┆ 01011    Eliminate
 _┆_
   1011      Answer
```

ⓐ

⑦

7⟌49

ⓑ

⑩

10⟌100

ⓒ

⑽⑩⑩

111⟌11100

Fill in the blanks.

Decimal	Binary
1 + 1 = ___	1 + 1 = ___

65

In the binary system, just as in the decimal system, certain mathematical manipulations are required when you subtract a larger number from a _____ number.

For example:
$$\begin{array}{r} 52 \\ - 38 \\ \hline \end{array}$$

⑧ is larger than ②

105

Solve the following:

$$\begin{array}{r} 111011 \\ - \quad 1001 \\ \hline \end{array}$$

145

In all numbering systems;

the number we are <u>dividing</u> is called the _____ ;

the number we are <u>dividing by</u> is called the _____ ;

the <u>answer</u> is called the _____ .

Decimal	Binary
1+1 = <u>2</u>	1+1 = 10

smaller

105	Add zeros	111011

$$- \; 001001$$

Complement 110111

Add   111011
         + 110111
       1 110010

Eliminate
           110010

dividend

divisor

quotient

26

There are only FOUR combinations of "0" and "1" that can be added together.

What are they?

66

In the BINARY System there is <u>only one</u> combination of 0 and 1 that will enable you to subtract a larger number from a smaller number.

What is it?

106

Solve the following:

```
  1011110
-   10000
```

146

Fill in the blanks with the words: Quotient, Dividend, Divisor

$$\underline{\qquad\qquad} \\ \underline{\qquad\qquad}\overline{)\underline{\qquad\qquad}}$$

26

$$0 + 0$$

$$1 + 0$$

$$0 + 1$$

$$1 + 1$$

66

$$\begin{array}{r} 0 \\ -1 \\ \hline \end{array}$$

106

Add zeros   1011110

$$-\,0010000$$

Complement   1110000

Add

$$\begin{array}{r} 1011110 \\ +\,1110000 \\ \hline 1\;\;1001110 \end{array}$$

Eliminate

1001110

146

Quotient

$$\text{Divisor} \,\overline{)\,\text{Dividend}}$$

27

Fill in the blanks.

Decimal	Binary
$0+0 = $ ___	$0+0 = $ ___
$1+0 = $ ___	$1+0 = $ ___
$0+1 = $ ___	$0+1 = $ ___
$1+1 = $ ___	$1+1 = $ ___

---

67 In the Decimal System

$$52 = 50 \quad \text{If we borrow 10 from } \textcircled{50} \text{ and} \quad 40$$
$$ + 2 \quad \text{add it to } \textcircled{2} \text{ we have} \longrightarrow + 12$$
$$\overline{52} \longleftarrow \quad \text{equivalent} \longrightarrow \overline{52}$$

Therefore $\underbrace{50 + 2}_{52} = \underbrace{40 + 12}_{52}$

GO TO NEXT FRAME

107

Solve the following using __two__ methods:

Subtraction by Borrowing	Subtraction through Complementing
1101	1101
- 10	- 10

147

In the BINARY System, if the divisor __goes into__ the dividend (divisor smaller than dividend) we place a __one (1)__ in the quotient.

If the divisor __does not go into__ the dividend (divisor larger than dividend) we place a __zero (0)__ in the quotient.

Place a (0) or (1) in each of the Quotients.

(a) $10\overline{)11}$ (b) $10\overline{)10}$ (c) $11\overline{)10}$ (d) $11\overline{)11}$

0	0
1	1
1	1
2	10

Subtraction by Borrowing	Subtraction through Complementing

Subtraction by Borrowing

```
      0 10
    1 1̸ 0̸ 1
  -     1 0
  ─────────
    1 0 1 1
```

Subtraction through Complementing

```
                            1101
                          - 0010
Complement — 1110          ──────
Add           ┊1101
            + ┊1110
            ──────────
             1┊1011
Eliminate     ┊1011
```

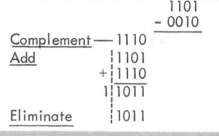

136

BINARY	Problem	Add Col. 1	Add Col. 2	ANSWER
$0+0=0$	②①	②①	②①	
$1+0=1$	1 0	1 0	1 0	
$0+1=1$	+ 0 1	+ 0 1	+ 0 1	
$1+1=10$		1	1 1	11

Solve the following: 01
                          + 10

```
        4 12                        5 17
 52  =  5̸ 2̸           67  =  6̸ 7
- 38   - 3 8         - 28   - 2 8
```

Borrow 10 in each of the following: 32   81
                                         - 6   - 63

Both methods of subtraction gave us the _____ answer.

⑪ is larger than ①
```
            0
(11) )̲(1)̲ 011
```

⑪ is larger than ⑩
```
           00
(11) )(10) 11
```

11 is smaller than 101
```
          001
(11) )(101) 1
```
STOP AFTER THE FIRST ONE (1).

Place the ones (1) and zeros (0) in each of the following quotients.

(a)   111)1011

(b)   10)100

STOP AFTER THE FIRST ONE

```
  01
+ 10
────
  11
```

```
  2  12
  З  2
-    6
────────
```

```
  7  11
  8  1
-  6  3
────────
```

same

ⓐ
```
        0001
111) 1011
```

ⓑ
```
      01
10) 100
```

BINARY   As we normally add, starting with the right hand column:

$0+0 = 1$ Add the following:
$1+0 = 1$
$0+1 = 1$ | 3 | 2 | 1 | | 3 | 2 | 1 |
$1+1 = 10$
     1 0 0   1 0 1
  + 1 0   + 1 0

69

In the BINARY System there is ONLY ONE combination of 0 and 1 that will require you to <u>subtract</u> a <u>larger</u> number <u>from a smaller</u> number. Write this combination.

109

Solve the following using either method.

     1110111
-    1000

149

Because zeros (0) in front of a number DO NOT change the value of the number,

We will not place any zeros (0) in the quotient until the first one (1) is reached.

Therefore: $\dfrac{01}{10)\overline{111}}$ becomes $\dfrac{1}{10)\overline{111}}$ and $\dfrac{0001}{111)\overline{1011}}$ becomes

                                                     $\dfrac{}{111)\overline{1011}}$

$$110$$
$$111$$

$$\begin{array}{r} 0 \\ -1 \\ \hline \end{array}$$

Subtraction by Borrowing

$$\begin{array}{ccccccc} & & 0 & 10 & & & \\ 1 & 1 & \cancel{1} & \cancel{0} & 1 & 1 & 1 \\ - & & & 1 & 0 & 0 & 0 \\ \hline 1 & 1 & 0 & 1 & 1 & 1 & 1 \end{array}$$

Subtraction through Complementing

$$\begin{array}{r} 1110111 \\ -\ 0001000 \\ \hline \end{array}$$

Complement — 1111000

Add
$$\begin{array}{r} 1110111 \\ +\ 1111000 \\ \hline 1\ 1101111 \end{array}$$

Eliminate   1101111

$$111\overline{)\begin{array}{r} 1 \\ 1011 \end{array}}$$

Starting with the right hand column
Add the following

$$
\begin{array}{r}
1\,0\,0\,1\,0\,1 \\
+\ \ 1\,0\,0\,1\,0 \\
\hline
\end{array}
\qquad\qquad
\begin{array}{r}
1\,0\,0\,1 \\
+\,1\,0\,0\,1\,0\,0 \\
\hline
\end{array}
$$

Just as we <u>borrow</u> in the Decimal System, we borrow in the Binary System.

Borrow From

Solve this binary subtraction problem.

<u>Solve the following BINARY problems</u>:

ⓐ	ⓑ	©
$\begin{array}{r}1011\\-\ 100\\\hline\end{array}$	$\begin{array}{r}1011\\+\ 100\\\hline\end{array}$	$\begin{array}{r}1110\\+\ 111\\\hline\end{array}$

Just like Binary Multiplication, BINARY DIVISION is the _____ as Decimal Division.

110111
101101

```
     0 10
  1  X  Ø
 -      1
 ─────────
  1  0  1
```

ⓐ

```
  1011
 - 100
 ─────
  0111
```

ⓑ

```
  1011
 + 100
 ─────
  1111
```

ⓒ

```
  1110
 + 111
 ─────
 10101
```

same

In the BINARY system $1 + 1 = 10$.

Therefore:

	1	and		1 0
	+ 1		+	1 0
	10			10 0

Add the following:

10	11
+ 10	+ 10

In subtraction, we <u>borrow</u> ONLY when we subtract a larger number from a smaller number.

```
      0→10
   1  X  Ø  1
   -     1  1
   1  0  1  0
```

Subtract the following

```
  1 1 0 1 1 1
- 1 0 1 0 1 1
```

We have learned BINARY ADDITION and SUBTRACTION. Now we will learn

Binary Multiplication

GO TO NEXT FRAME

BINARY DIVISION

Decimal

```
       2
  12)27
     24
      3  remainder
```

Binary

```
      1
  10)11
     10
      1  remainder
```

GO TO NEXT FRAME

143

31

100
101

71

```
      0  10
   1  1̸  0̸  1  1  1
 - 1  0  1  0  1  1
   ─────────────────
         1  1  0  0
```

111

151

In the DECIMAL system, when we add two numbers whose sum has two

digits $\left(\begin{array}{c} 5 \\ +6 \\ \hline 11 \end{array}\right)$ we add the first digit (1) to the next column.

Add the following DECIMAL numbers:

5	15	234	873
+ 5	+ 5	+ 29	+ 629

When we BORROW we must always borrow from the next (1). We
cannot borrow from a (0).

In this problem   1 1 0   we borrow from
       −   1

In this problem   1 1 0 0   we borrow from
       −   1

Circle the (1) we bor-
row from in this
problem.

     1 0 1 0 0 0
     −   1

In all numbering systems, the number we are MULTIPLYING
is called the MULTIPLICAND.

Decimal		Binary	All Systems

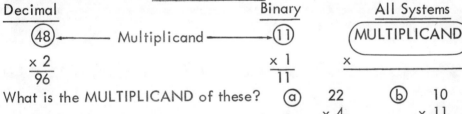

What is the MULTIPLICAND of these?   ⓐ   22   ⓑ   10
                                     × 4   × 11
                                      88   110

Decimal

       24   11
16)387   10)111
    32   10
    67   11
    64   10
     3 remainder   1 remainder

Solve

10)110

32

10
20
263
1502

72

1 0 ① 0 0 0
–　　　　　1
———————————

112

ⓐ　22
ⓑ　10

152

```
      11
10)110
   10
   ——
   10
   10
   ——
    0  remainder
```

In the BINARY system, when we add two numbers whose sum has two

digits $\left(\begin{array}{c} 1 \\ +1 \\ \hline 10 \end{array} \right)$ we <u>also</u> add the <u>first digit</u> ⓵ 0 to the next column.

In the BINARY SYSTEM, there is only <u>ONE</u> combination whose sum has two digits. Write this combination and its sum.

---

73 Let us Solve this Problem $\left(\text{remember} \begin{array}{c} 10 \\ -1 \\ \hline 1 \end{array} \right)$

Problem ⟶ Borrow from Col. 4

0⟵10

101000   1 0 ⑴ Ø 0 0

−   1   −   1

1. We borrow (1) from col. 4

$1 - 1 = 0$

2. The 0 in <u>col.</u> 3 becomes

10

Shade in the number that we are borrowing from in col. 4.

113

$$\begin{array}{r} 106 \\ \times\ 5 \\ \hline 530 \end{array} \qquad \begin{array}{r} 101 \\ \times\ 10 \\ \hline 1010 \end{array}$$

In the above examples, 106 and 101 are called the _____.

153

<u>S</u>olve:

$11\overline{)110110}$

$$\begin{array}{r} 1 \\ +\ 1 \\ \hline 10 \end{array}$$

Borrow from Col. 4

0↔10

1 0 1̸ 0̸ 0 0

−   1

multiplicand

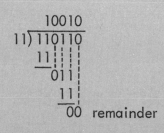

```
        10010
    11) 110110
        11
        ───
         011
         11
        ────
          00   remainder
```

In the BINARY System -- Add the first column

column   1

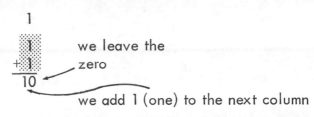

we leave the zero

we add 1 (one) to the next column

GO TO NEXT FRAME

Problem→ Borrow from Col. 4 → Borrow from Col. 3   1. We borrow from Col. 3

                  0←10   0 ⑩ 10 $10 - 1 = 1$

101000 1 0 ① Ø 0 0 1 0 ⅟ Ø Ø 0 2. The 0 in Col.

-   1 -   1 -   1   2 becomes 10

Circle the number that the number we are borrowing from becomes (in Col. 3).

Circle the multiplicand in each of the following:

ⓐ	ⓑ	ⓒ
32	111	100
× 3	× 10	× 111
96	1110	11100

Solve:

        11) 101011

74

Borrow from Col. 3

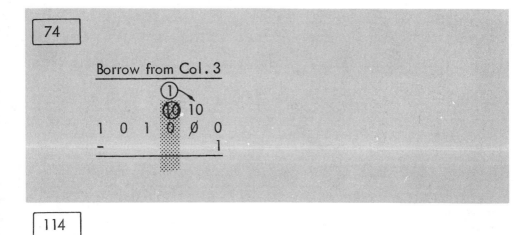

114

ⓐ
㉜
× 3
96

ⓑ
⑴⑴⑴
× 10
1110

ⓒ
⑴⓪⓪
× 111
11100

154

```
        1110
11) 101011
    011
   0100
     11
   00011
     11
     01 remainder
```

35

When Adding BINARY numbers we will designate the first digit that we add to the next column by circling it.

Therefore: Add Col. 1

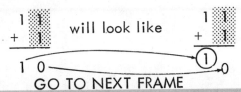

```
  1 1                    1 1
+   1    will look like +  1
-----                   -----
  1 0                   (1)0
```

GO TO NEXT FRAME

75

Problem	→ Bor. from Col. 4	→ Bor. from Col. 3	→ Bor. from Col. 2
	0←10	1 ↖ 0 (10) 10	1 1 ↖ 0 10 (10) 10
101000	1 0 (1) 0 0 0	1 0 1 0 0 0	1 0 1 0 0 0
− 1	− 1	− 1	− 1

1. We borrow from Col. 2. 10 − 1 = 1
2. The 0 in Col. 1 becomes 10.

When we borrow from Col. 2, we change the number in Col. 1. Circle this new number.

115 In all numbering systems, the number we are MULTIPLYING BY is called the MULTIPLIER.

Decimal		Binary	All Systems
48		11	MULTIPLICAND
×(2)	← Multiplier →	×(1)	×(MULTIPLIER)
96		11	

What is the MULTIPLIER of these? (a) 22 × 4 = 88   (b) 10 × 11 = 110

155

Solve:

101)11110

35

75

Borrow from Col. 3

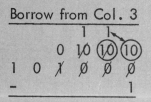

115

(a)　4

(b)　11

155

```
           110
101)  11110
       101
       ‾‾‾‾
       101
       101
       ‾‾‾‾
        00  remainder
```

Using this designation we will solve a problem:

Problem	Add Col. 1	Add Col. 2	Add Col. 3	Answer

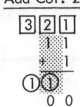

Problem
```
   1 1
 +   1
 -----
```

Add Col. 1
```
 [3][2][1]
   1  1
 +    1
 -----
    ①
       0
```

Add Col. 2
```
 [3][2][1]
    1  1
  +    1
 ------
  ①①
      0 0
```

Add Col. 3
```
 [3][2][1]
     1 1
   +   1
 ------
  ①①
     1 0 0
```

Answer

100

Solve:
```
  101
 + 11
 ----
```

The problem now looks like this.

```
        1  1
     0 1̸0 1̸0 10
  1  0 1̸  0̸  0̸  0̸
  -               1
  -----------------
```

What is the solution?

```
  106          101
 ×  5         × 10
 -----        -----
  530         1010
```

In the above examples, 5 and 10 are called the _____.

Solve:

```
1011) 1001011
```

1000

100111

multiplier

```
           110
1011) 1001011
      1011
      001111
      1011
       1001  remainder
```

roblem	Add Col. 1	Add Col. 2	Add Col. 3	Add Col. 4	Add Col. 5
5 4 3 2 1	5 4 3 2 1	5 4 3 2 1	5 4 3 2 1	5 4 3 2 1	5 4 3 2 1
1 1 0 1	1 1 0 1	1 1 0 1	1 1 0 1	1 1 0 1	1 1 0 1
+ 1 0 1	+ 1 0 1	+ 1 0 1	+ 1 0 1	+ 1 0 1	+ 1 0 1
	①	①	① ①	①① ①	①① ①
	0	1 0	0 1 0	0 0 1 0	1 0 0 1 0

Add the following: 1110 + 11 = _ ; 1011 + 101 = _   Answer 10010

77

olve

```
  1100
-    1
```

117

Circle the multiplier in each of the following:

ⓐ	ⓑ	ⓒ
32	111	100
× 3	× 10	× 111
96	1110	11100

157

ADD:

```
  110
   10
 1011
```

10001

10000

$$\begin{array}{r} 1\ 0\ 1\ 0 \\ 1\ 1\ 0\ 0 \\ -\quad\quad\ 1 \\ \hline 1\ 0\ 1\ 1 \end{array}$$

ⓐ

$$\begin{array}{r} 32 \\ \times 3 \\ \hline 96 \end{array}$$

ⓑ

$$\begin{array}{r} 111 \\ \times 10 \\ \hline 1110 \end{array}$$

ⓒ

$$\begin{array}{r} 100 \\ \times 111 \\ \hline 11100 \end{array}$$

$$\begin{array}{r} 110 \\ 10 \\ 1011 \\ \hline \end{array}$$

1000   Partial sum

$$\begin{array}{r} 1011 \\ \hline 10011 \end{array}$$

Problem	Add Col. 1	Add Col. 2	Add Col. 3	Add Col. 4	Answer
1011 + 10	1011 + 10	1011 + 10	1011 + 10	1011 + 10	
		①	①	①	
	1	01	101	1101	1101

Add the following:

```
10011        10100
  101        10111
-----        -----
```

Solve

```
  11001
-   110
```

In all numbering systems, the number we are <u>multiplying</u> is called the _____ and the number we are <u>multiplying by</u> is called the _____ .

SUBTRACT:

```
  110010
-  10111
```

11000

101011

```
        1
    0 10 10
  1  1̸  0̸  0̸  1
 -      1  1  0
  1  0  0  1  1
```

multiplicand

multiplier

```
  110010
 - 10111
  011011
```

Solve the following:

110011	110111	100011
+ 100100	+ 1010	+ 101

79   In many problems, we will <u>borrow</u> more than once.

Problem→<u>Subt. Col. 1</u>   1. We borrow from <u>Col. 2</u>
                                          1 - 1 = 0

Borrow
                    0 10   2. The 0 in <u>Col. 1</u> becomes 10.
1110   1 1 (1) Ø
- 11   -   1 1

Subtract Col. 1.

119   The <u>ANSWER</u> to multiplying problems, in all numbering systems, is called the <u>PRODUCT</u>.

Decimal	Binary	All Systems
48	11	MULTIPLICAND
× 2	× 1	× MULTIPLIER
(96) ←——— Product ———→ (11)		(PRODUCT)

What is the PRODUCT of these?   (a)   22   (b)   10
                                       × 4   × 11
                                       88   110

159

MULTIPLY:

(a)   110   (b)   101
      × 101   × 111

39

1010111
1000001
101000

79

1

119

ⓐ 88
ⓑ 110

159

ⓐ   110
     × 101
     ─────
       110
      1100
     ─────
     11110

ⓑ   101
     × 111
     ─────
       101
       101
     ─────
      1111
       101
     ─────
     100011

In the BINARY system, we may want to add three (3) or more numbers.

110	1110	10
101	101	1
10	1000	101
	1111	100
		111

GO TO NEXT FRAME

Problem→Subt. Col. 1→Subt. Col. 2

1. We borrow from Col. 3
   1 – 1 = 0

2. The 0 in Col. 2 becomes 10.

Subtract Col. 2.

106	101
× 5	× 10
530	1010

In these examples, 530 and 1010 are called the _____.

(a) 11011
     + 1011

(b) 10110
     – 1001

(c) 110) 10110

1

product

ⓐ 100110

ⓑ 1101

ⓒ 11 and 100 remainder

GO TO FRAME 41 ON PAGE 83

GO TO FRAME 81 ON PAGE 83

GO TO FRAME 121 ON PAGE 83

GO TO CHAPTER IV ON NEXT PAGE

NOTES

Chapter IV   Fractional Numbers

Fractional numbers are numbers less-than-one and are used extensively in computers. Chapter IV describes fractional numbers and teaches the student how to convert fractional numbers between systems. It also teaches the student how to add, subtract, multiply and divide mixed numbers in the binary system. A mixed number contains a whole number and a fractional number.

Chapter Outline

IV   Fractional Numbers
1. What are Fractional Numbers
2. Converting Fractional Numbers
3. Binary Arithmetic with Mixed Numbers

NOW, TURN THE PAGE AND READ FRAME 1 OF CHAPTER IV.

NOTES

What are Fractional Numbers

GO TO NEXT FRAME

Convert the following Decimal Whole Number to a Binary Whole Number.

26_{10} — This subscript tells us that we are using number 26 in the decimal system

First, let us review converting whole BINARY numbers to whole DECIMAL numbers.

Every digit in a Binary number has a PLACE.

etc.	4	3	2	1	0	place
	1	0	0	1	1	Binary Whole number

What is the place of the (1) in 100_2?

(a) Decimal

235.36
- 42.72

(b) Binary

100.10
- 10.01

23

```
2) 26
 2) 13     0
  2) 6     1
   2) 3    0
    2) 1   1
      0    1
           1 1 0 1 0
```

45

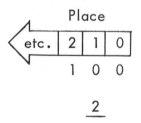

Place

etc. | 2 | 1 | 0
     1   0   0

2

67

ⓐ 192.64

ⓑ 10.01

All <u>numbers</u> are made up of combinations of whole numbers
(numbers larger than one (1)) and fractional numbers (numbers smaller than one (1)).

WHOLE NUMBER	FRACTIONAL NUMBER
34	1/2
248.	741
2	3/4
4.	75

GO TO NEXT FRAME

24

Convert the following to binary.

35_{10}

46   Each <u>Binary</u> <u>digit</u> has a decimal value equal to

the (Digit) times 2 to the (place)

<u>Binary Digit</u>

$$1 = 1(2^0)$$

$$1\,0 = 0(2^0) + 1(2^1)$$

$$1\,0\,0 = 0(2^0) + 0(2^1) + \underline{\quad} (\underline{\quad})$$

68

Solve the following:

ⓐ	ⓑ	ⓒ	ⓓ
111.011	1100.101	11.100	11.100
+ 11.1	− 10.11	+10.01	−10.01
+ 10.101			

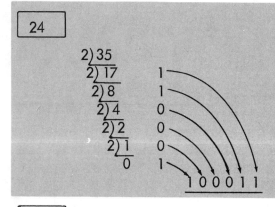

$$1(2^2)$$

ⓐ   1101.100

ⓑ   1001.111

ⓒ   101.110

ⓓ   1.010

3

In the Decimal system, FRACTIONAL NUMBERS (Numbers LESS than ONE (1)) are expressed as FRACTIONS (1/2, 1/4, 1/5) or as numbers to the RIGHT of the BASE POINT.

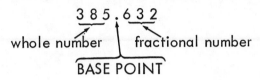

$$3\ 8\ 5\ .\ 6\ 3\ 2$$

whole number | fractional number

BASE POINT

GO TO NEXT FRAME

25

Now, let us learn how to convert FRACTIONAL NUMBERS from Decimal to Binary.

Remember, to convert fractional numbers from Decimal to Binary, all decimal fractions must be changed to decimal _____ _____ numbers.

47

The Decimal values of each of the BINARY digits is illustrated below:

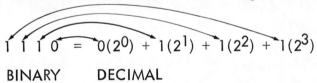

$$1\ 1\ 1\ 0\ =\ 0(2^0)\ +\ 1(2^1)\ +\ 1(2^2)\ +\ 1(2^3)$$

BINARY   DECIMAL

GO TO NEXT FRAME

69

BINARY MULTIPLICATION with mixed numbers is also the same as with Decimal Multiplication.

1. The number of FRACTIONAL PLACES of Multiplicand and multiplier are added.

2. This number locates the base point in the product.

GO TO NEXT FRAME

3

25

base point

47

69

FRACTIONAL NUMBERS

Fractions		Base Point numbers
$\frac{1}{2}$	can be expressed as	.5
$\frac{1}{4}$	can be expressed as	.25
$5\frac{1}{4}$	can be expressed as	5.25
$27\frac{1}{4}$	can be expressed as	_____ .

26

The Decimal fractional BASE POINT Number can now be converted to Binary. This is done in two (2) steps which will be explained more fully.

STEP I — <u>Multiply</u> the Decimal fractional number <u>by 2</u> (continue to zero or required number of places).

STEP II — <u>Sequence</u> the <u>overflows</u>.

GO TO NEXT FRAME

48

To convert a BINARY number to its DECIMAL equivalent three steps are performed.

Example

STEP I — Expand $1\ 1\ 0 = 0(2^0) + 1(2^1) + 1(2^2)$

STEP II — Multiply $1\ 1\ 0 = \quad 0 \quad + \quad 2 \quad + \quad 4$

STEP III — Add $1\ 1\ 0 = \quad 6$

BINARY = DECIMAL

GO TO NEXT FRAME

70

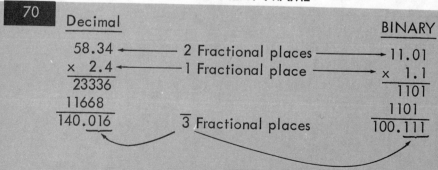

Decimal		BINARY
58.34 ◄——— 2 Fractional places ———►		11.01
× 2.4 ◄——— 1 Fractional place ———►		× 1.1
23336		1101
11668		1101
140.016 3 Fractional places		100.111

GO TO NEXT FRAME

173

4

27.25

26

48

70

174

Circle the <u>whole number</u> of each of the following:

(a)   (b)   (c)   (d)

35.38 $21\frac{1}{5}$ 85   0.334

27

STEP 1 - Multiply the Decimal number by 2.

.625 ←——Decimal Fractional number

× 2

overflow —→ ①.250

GO TO NEXT FRAME

49

Convert 1011_2 to Decimal.

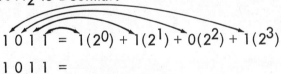

$1\ 0\ 1\ 1\ =\ 1(2^0)+1(2^1)+0(2^2)+1(2^3)$

$1\ 0\ 1\ 1\ =\ \underline{\hphantom{xxxxxx}}$

71

Write the <u>total</u> number of FRACTIONAL places in each of the following.

(a)   28.25   (b)   111.0   (c)   110.0011
      × 2.13   × 1.01   ×   10

      ____   ____   ____

5

ⓐ ㉟.38

ⓑ ㉑ $\frac{1}{5}$

ⓒ (85)

ⓓ ⓪.334

27

49

EXPAND	$1011 = 1(2^0) + 1(2^1) + 0(2^2) + 1(2^3)$
MULTIPLY	$1011 = 1 + 2 + 0 + 8$
ADD	$1011 = 11$

71

ⓐ 4

ⓑ 3

ⓒ 4

6

Circle the <u>fractional number</u> of each of the following:

      ⓐ   ⓑ   ⓒ   ⓓ

   247.6   385 $22\frac{1}{2}$ $\frac{1}{3}$

---

28   STEP I – Keep multiplying the <u>fractional product</u> by 2.

$$
\begin{array}{r}
.625 \\
\times\ \ 2 \\
\hline
\text{overflow}\rightarrow \textcircled{1}.250 \\
\times\ \ 2 \\
\hline
\end{array}
\quad (.250 \text{ is the fractional product})
$$

ⓐ   What is the fractional product?

ⓑ   What is the overflow?

50

Convert 1100_2 to Decimal.

72

Place the <u>base point</u> in the product of each of the following:

ⓐ
$$
\begin{array}{r}
35.1 \\
\times\ 2.1 \\
\hline
351 \\
702 \\
\hline
7371
\end{array}
$$

ⓑ
$$
\begin{array}{r}
11.11 \\
\times\ \ 101 \\
\hline
1111 \\
11110 \\
\hline
1001011
\end{array}
$$

ⓒ
$$
\begin{array}{r}
101 \\
\times\ 111 \\
\hline
101 \\
101 \\
101 \\
\hline
100011
\end{array}
$$

ⓐ   ⓑ   ⓒ   ⓓ

247.⑥   385◯ $22\left(\frac{1}{2}\right)$ $\left(\frac{1}{3}\right)$

28

ⓐ   .500

ⓑ   0

50

EXPAND	$1100 = 0(2^0) + 0(2^1) + 1(2^2) + 1(2^3)$
MULTIPLY	$1100 = \quad 0 \quad + \quad 0 \quad + \quad 4 \quad + \quad 8$
ADD	$1100 = \quad 12$

72

ⓐ   73.71

ⓑ   10010.11

ⓒ   100011.

Because the BINARY system uses only base point numbers, all decimal fractions must be changed to decimal base point numbers before we can convert a decimal number to a binary number.

GO TO NEXT FRAME

STEP I - Keep multiplying the fractional product by 2.

```
              .625
            x   2
overflow →①.250
            x   2
           ⓪.500
            x   2
              .
```

Converting MIXED NUMBERS from BINARY to DECIMAL is the same as converting whole numbers.

STEP I   - EXPAND

STEP II   - MULTIPLY

STEP III - ADD

GO TO NEXT FRAME

Solve the following:

```
    110.1
  x 1.01
```

29

1.000

51

73

$$
\begin{array}{r}
1\,1\,0\,.\,1 \\
\times\;\;1\,.\,0\,1 \\
\hline
1\,1\,0\,1 \\
1\,1\,0\,1\,0\;\;\; \\
\hline
1\,0\,0\,0\,.\,0\,0\,1 \\
\end{array}
$$

| 8 | In the DECIMAL system, let us change a Fraction |

to a ⟶ base point number.

$\frac{1}{2}$ means: Divide 1 by 2

$\frac{1}{4}$ means: Divide 1 by 4

$\frac{3}{8}$ means: Divide ___ by ___

| 30 | STEP I – Keep multiplying the fractional product by 2. |

You stop multiplying when

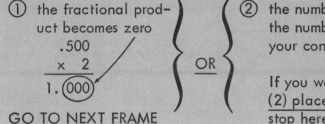

① the fractional prod-
uct becomes zero

.500
× 2
1.(000)

GO TO NEXT FRAME

OR

② the number of overflows equals
the number of places desired in
your conversion.

overflow   .625
            × 2
If you want two   1.250
(2) places,   × 2
stop here ⟶   0.500

| 52 | Let us assign places. |

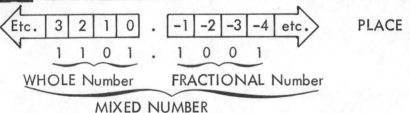

Etc. | 3 | 2 | 1 | 0 | . | -1 | -2 | -3 | -4 | etc.   PLACE

1   1   0   1   .   1   0   0   1

WHOLE Number   FRACTIONAL Number

MIXED NUMBER

What is the PLACE of the two ONES (1) on either side of the
base point?

| 74 | |

Solve the following:

111.001
× .0101

3
8

0
−1

```
    1 1 1 . 0 0 1
  ×     . 0 1 0 1
  ─────────────────
      1 1 1 0 0 1
  1 1 1 0 0 1 0
  ─────────────────
  1 0 . 0 0 1 1 1 0 1
```

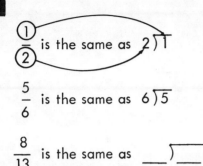

$\dfrac{1}{2}$ is the same as $2\overline{)1}$

$\dfrac{5}{6}$ is the same as $6\overline{)5}$

$\dfrac{8}{13}$ is the same as $\underline{}\overline{)\underline{}}$

---

31   <u>STEP 1</u> – Multiply by 2.   <u>STEP 2</u> – Sequence the overflows.

```
   .625                          .625
  × 2                           × 2
 1.250                         1.250
  × 2                           × 2
 0.500    Base                 0.500
  × 2     Point                 × 2
 1.000    placed              1.000
          here ──► .1 0 1 ◄──── This is your BINARY number.
```

The BINARY equivalent of the DECIMAL number .625 is _____.

53

Notice that the WHOLE number PLACE starts with 0, but the
FRACTIONAL number PLACE starts with −1.

Fill in the places.

---

75   <u>BINARY DIVISION</u> with <u>mixed numbers</u> is the same as with
<u>Decimal Division.</u>

1. Move the base point of the DIVISOR to the $1.\underset{\smile}{10}\,\overline{)111.001}$
   right to make it a whole number.
2. Move the base point of the DIVIDEND the $1.\underset{\smile}{10}\,\overline{)111.\underset{\smile}{00}.1}$
   same number of places to the right.
3. Place the base point of the QUOTIENT $1.\underset{\smile}{10}\,\overline{)111.\underset{\smile}{00}.1}$
   above the base point of the Dividend.
4. Solve the problem.

                GO TO NEXT FRAME

$$13\overline{)8}$$

.101

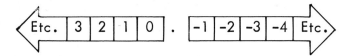

10

$\frac{1}{2}$ is the same as $2\overline{)1}$

$$2\overline{)1.00}.5$$
$$\underline{1\ 0}$$

Therefore $\frac{1}{2}$ = .5

What is the Base Point number that is the equivalent of $\frac{3}{4}$?

---

32   What is the BINARY equivalent of the Decimal .375?

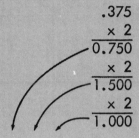

$$.375$$
$$\underline{\times\ 2}$$
$$0.750$$
$$\underline{\times\ 2}$$
$$1.500$$
$$\underline{\times\ 2}$$
$$1.000$$

---

54   Convert 110.11_2 to Decimal

STEP I - EXPAND

$$1\ 1\ 0\ .\ 1\ 1_2 = \underline{}(\underline{}) + \underline{}(\underline{}) + \underline{}(\underline{})$$

Fill in the WHOLE Number EXPANSION.

76

Decimal	Binary

$$2.61.1$$
$$3.8\overline{)10.0\ 0}1.01\overline{)10.01\ 0}$$
$$\underline{7\ 6}\underline{1\ 01}$$
$$2\ 4\ 01\ 00\ 0$$
$$\underline{2\ 2\ 8}\underline{10\ 1}$$
$$0\ 01\ 1$$

GO TO NEXT FRAME

185

$$\begin{array}{r} .75 \\ 4\overline{)3.00} \end{array}$$

.75

.011

$$\underline{0}(2^{\underline{0}}) + \underline{1}(2^{\underline{1}}) + \underline{1}(2^{\underline{2}})$$

Change each of these fractions to a base point number.

(a)

$\dfrac{1}{5}$

(b)

$\dfrac{1}{4}$

(c)

$\dfrac{3}{8}$

33

What is the BINARY equivalent of the Decimal $.742_{10}$ computed to two places?

$$
\begin{array}{r}
.742 \\
\times\ 2 \\
\hline
1.484 \\
\times\ 2 \\
\hline
0.968
\end{array}
$$

55   Convert 110.11_2 to Decimal

STEP I - EXPAND

$110 . 1\ 1_2 = \underline{\quad}(\underline{\quad}) + \underline{\quad}(\underline{\quad}) + 0(2^0) + 1(2^1) + 1(2^2)$

Fill in the FRACTIONAL Number Expansion.

77

Place the BASE POINT in the quotient of each of the following: (do not solve problem)

(a)

$1.1) \overline{10.0\,01}$

(b)

$110) \overline{111.001}$

(c)

$.111.) \overline{11.011}$

11

(a) .2
(b) .25
(c) .375

33

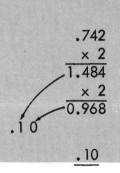

$$.742$$
$$\times\ 2$$
$$\overline{1.484}$$
$$\times\ 2$$
$$\overline{0.968}$$

.1 0

.10

55

$$\underline{\ 1\ }(\underline{2^{-2}}) + \underline{\ 1\ }(\underline{2^{-1}})$$

77

(a) 1.1.) 10.0.01

(b) 110) 111.001

(c) .111.) 11.011.

When changing a fraction to a base point number, often a long stream
of numbers appear:

For Example:
$$\frac{5}{6} = .833333 \ldots \ldots \ldots \text{ etc.}$$

$$\frac{7}{13} = .538461 \ldots \ldots \ldots \text{ etc.}$$

GO TO NEXT FRAME

34

What is the BINARY equivalent of the decimal $.836_{10}$ computed to
three places?

56

$$2^{-1} = \frac{1}{2^1} = \frac{1}{2}$$

$$2^{-2} = \frac{1}{2^2} = \frac{1}{4}$$

$$2^{-3} = \frac{1}{2^3} = \frac{1}{8}$$

$$2^{-4} = \underline{} = \underline{}$$

78

LOCATE the new BASE POINT in the dividend and quotient of each
of the following:

       (a)   (b)   (c)

$$1.11. \overline{)1.1011} \qquad 1.001. \overline{)110.1} \qquad 10.0. \overline{).00110}$$

34

```
        .836
       ×  2
      ------
      1.672
       ×  2
      ------
      1.344
       ×  2
      ------
      0.688
  .1  1  0
```

56

$$\frac{1}{2^4} = \frac{1}{16}$$

78

(a) $1.11\overline{\smash{)}1.10.11}$

(b) $1.001\overline{\smash{)}110.100}$

(c) $10.0\overline{\smash{)}0.0110}$

13

The importance of each place to the right of the base point becomes less and less.

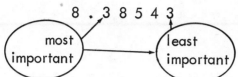

$$8 \cdot 3\ 8\ 5\ 4\ 3$$

most important → least important

In the above number, which is more important, 5 or 4?   Why?

35

Convert $.134_{10}$ to a BINARY number computed to two places.

57   STEP I – EXPAND

$$110.11_2 = 1(2^{-2}) + 1(2^{-1}) + 0(2^0) + 1(2^1) + 1(2^2)$$

$$1\left(\frac{1}{2^2}\right) + 1\left(\frac{1}{2^1}\right) + 0(2^0) + 1(2^1) + 1(2^2)$$

STEP II – MULTIPLY

$$110.11_2 = 1/4 + 1/2 + \underline{\hspace{1cm}} + \underline{\hspace{1cm}} + \underline{\hspace{1cm}}$$

79

LOCATE the new BASE POINT in the divisor, dividend, and quotient of each of the following:

(a)   (b)   (c)

$1.11 \overline{)1001}$ $.101 \overline{)11.1}$ $.10 \overline{)10}$

5

It is closer to the base point

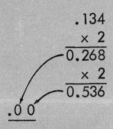

$$\begin{array}{r} .134 \\ \times\ 2 \\ \hline 0.268 \\ \times\ 2 \\ \hline 0.536 \end{array}$$

.0 0

0 + 2 + 4

ⓐ   1.11.) 1001.00.

ⓑ   .101.) 11.100.

ⓒ   .10.) 10.00.

Because each successive place to the right of the base point becomes less important, we often will <u>limit</u> the number of places.

For Example:

If we limit to 3 places --- 8.38543 becomes 8.385

6.28943 becomes 6.289

.08021 becomes _____

Convert $\frac{1}{4}$ to Binary.

STEP I - EXPAND

$$110.11_2 = 1\left(\frac{1}{2^2}\right) + 1\left(\frac{1}{2^1}\right) + 0(2^0) + 1(2^1) + 1(2^2)$$

STEP II - MULTIPLY

$$110.11_2 = 1/4 + 1/2 + 0 + 2 + 4$$

STEP III - ADD

$$110.11_2 = \underline{\hspace{2cm}} {}_{10}$$

Solve the following:

$$10.1 \overline{)\,10.101}$$

.080

$$\frac{1}{4} = 4\overline{)1.00}^{.25}$$

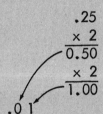

$$.25$$
$$\times\ 2$$
$$\overline{0.50}$$
$$\times\ 2$$
$$\overline{1.00}$$

.0 1

$$2\ +\ 4\ =\ 6$$
$$1/4 + 1/2\ =\ \frac{3}{4}$$
$$6\frac{3}{4}$$

$$6\frac{3}{4}\ \text{or}\ 6.75$$

$$10.1\overline{)10.1\ 01}^{1.00}$$
$$\underline{10\ 1}$$
$$01$$

When limiting to a given number of places, if the number in the next place is 5 or higher we ADD ONE (1) to our LAST GIVEN PLACE. If not we accept the last given place as it is.

If we limit to 2 places --- 8.38543 becomes 8.39
6.28943 becomes 6.29
.08021 becomes .08
3.67704 becomes _____ Why?

37

Convert $\frac{5}{6}$ to Binary and limit to 3 places.

59   Convert 11.01101_2 to DECIMAL

STEP I - Expand

$$11.011 01_2 = 1\left(\frac{1}{2^5}\right) + 0\left(\frac{1}{2^4}\right) + 1\left(\frac{1}{2^3}\right) + 1\left(\frac{1}{2^2}\right) + 0\left(\frac{1}{2^1}\right)$$
$$+ 1(2^0) + 1(2^1)$$

$11.011 01_2 =$ _____ 10

81

Solve the following:

$$101\overline{)111.001}$$

3.68

Because the number in the next place is 5 or higher.

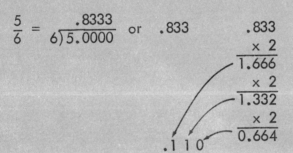

$$\frac{5}{6} = 6\overline{)5.0000}^{\,.8333} \quad \text{or} \quad .833$$

$$
\begin{array}{r}
.833 \\
\times\ 2 \\
\hline
1.666 \\
\times\ 2 \\
\hline
1.332 \\
\times\ 2 \\
\hline
0.664
\end{array}
$$

.1 1 0

STEP II – Multiply
$$= \frac{1}{32} + \frac{1}{8} + \frac{1}{4} + 1 + 2$$

STEP III – Add
$$= \frac{1}{32} + \frac{4}{32} + \frac{8}{32} + 3 \qquad\qquad = 3\frac{13}{32}$$
$$= \frac{13}{32} + 3 \qquad\qquad \text{or} \quad 3.41_{10}$$

$$
\begin{array}{r}
.406 \\
32\overline{)13.000} \\
12\ 8 \\
\hline
200
\end{array}
$$

$$
\begin{array}{r}
1.011 \\
101\overline{)111.001} \\
101 \\
\hline
10\ 00 \\
1\ 01 \\
\hline
0\ 111 \\
101 \\
\hline
10
\end{array}
$$

Limit each of the following to three (3) places.

ⓐ	ⓑ	ⓒ	ⓓ
243.8654	3.8942	1.86283	21.66666

We have mentioned that to convert a DECIMAL Mixed number to a BINARY Mixed number, we:
1. Convert the WHOLE NUMBER
2. Convert the FRACTIONAL NUMBER
3. Add the TWO

BINARY WHOLE NUMBER   1101
BINARY FRACTIONAL NUMBER   .101

ADD: _____

Convert 101.101_2 to Decimal

Solve the following:

$$.010\overline{)11.0011}$$

(a)   243.865

(b)   3.894

(c)   1.863

(d)   21.667

38

1101.101

60

STEP I - Expand
$$1\left(\frac{1}{2^3}\right) + 1\left(\frac{1}{2^1}\right) + 1(2^0) + 1(2^2)$$

STEP II - Multiply
$$\frac{1}{8} + \frac{1}{2} + 1 + 4$$

STEP III - Add $\frac{5}{8} + 5 = 5\frac{5}{8}$ or 5.625

82

$$
\begin{array}{r}
1\ 100.1 \\
.010.\overline{)11.001.1} \\
10 \\
\overline{1\ 0} \\
1\ 0 \\
\overline{01\ 1} \\
1\ 0 \\
\overline{1}
\end{array}
$$

17

Change each of these <u>Fractions</u> to a <u>Base Point Number</u> and limit to
two (2) places.

(a)

$\dfrac{5}{6}$

(b)

$\dfrac{2}{3}$

(c)

$\dfrac{9}{13}$

39

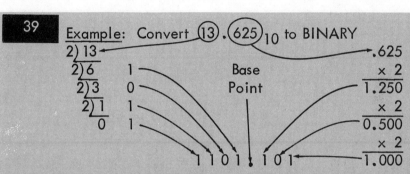

Example: Convert ⑬.⑥㉕$_{10}$ to BINARY

What is the BINARY EQUIVALENT of 13.625_{10}?

61

Convert 110.011_2 to Decimal

83

ADD the following:

(a) 11.01
   + 1.11

(b) 1.001
   + 1.1

(c) 111
   + 10
   + 11

(a) $6\overline{)5.000}$ = .833⌐ or .83

(b) $3\overline{)2.000}$ = .666⌐ or .67

(c) $13\overline{)9.000}$ = .692⌐ or .69

BASE POINT

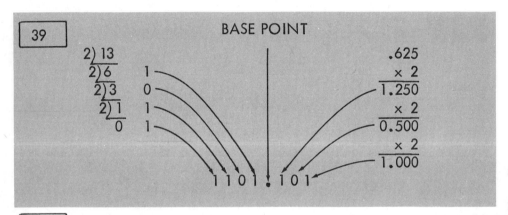

STEP I – Expand

$$1\left(\frac{1}{2^3}\right) + 1\left(\frac{1}{2^2}\right) + 1(2^1) + 1(2^2)$$

STEP II – Multiply

$$\frac{1}{8} + \frac{1}{4} + 2 + 4$$

STEP III – Add $\quad \frac{3}{8} + 6 = 6\frac{3}{8}$ or 6.38

(a)
```
  11.01
+  1.11
-------
 101.00
```

(b)
```
  1.001      1.001
+   1.1  =  +  1.1
--------    -------
            10.101
```

(c)
```
   111
+   10
------
  1001
+   11
------
  1100
```

Converting Fractional Numbers

GO TO NEXT FRAME

40

Convert 16.25_{10} to BINARY

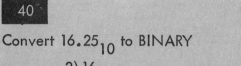

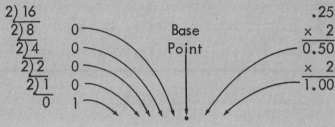

62.

Convert 38.672_{10} to BINARY (compute to 2 places)

84.

Solve the following:

(a) 1.110
     − .100

(b) 11.001
     − 10.10

(c) 1000.1
     −1.0001

40

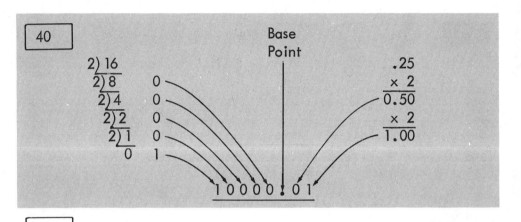

```
2) 16
 2) 8     0
  2) 4    0
   2) 2   0
    2) 1  0
     0    1
```

Base
Point

```
.25
× 2
0.50
× 2
1.00
```

1 0 0 0 0 . 0 1

62

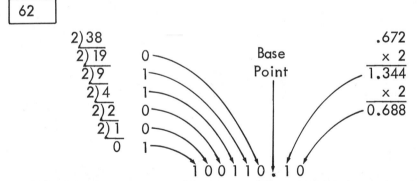

```
2) 38
 2) 19    0
  2) 9    1
   2) 4   1
    2) 2  0
     2) 1 0
      0   1
```

Base
Point

```
.672
× 2
1.344
× 2
0.688
```

1 0 0 1 1 0 . 1 0

84

   (a)   1.110   (b)   11.001   (c)   1000.1

```
(a)  1.110        (b)  11.001        (c)  1000.1
    - .100           -10.10            - 1.0001
     1.010            00.101           111.0111
```

19

A <u>MIXED NUMBER</u> is a number that contains a WHOLE NUMBER and
a <u>FRACTIONAL NUMBER</u>.

<u>Circle the mixed numbers</u>

ⓐ   ⓑ   ⓒ   ⓓ   ⓔ

38.58 $21\frac{1}{2}$ 35   .030   21

---

41   Convert $14\frac{2}{7}$ to BINARY (compute to 3 places)

14.286

$\frac{2}{7} = 7\overline{)2.0000}$ .2857   or   .286

$2\overline{)14}$
$2\overline{)7}$ 0
$2\overline{)3}$ 1
$2\overline{)1}$ 1
0   1

.286
× 2
_____
0.572
× 2
_____
1.144
× 2
_____
0.288

63

Convert $27\frac{3}{7}$ to BINARY (compute to 3 places)

85.

Solve the following:

ⓐ   11.11
    × 10.1

ⓑ   11.1
    × 1.11

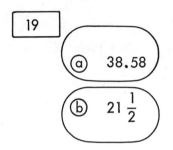
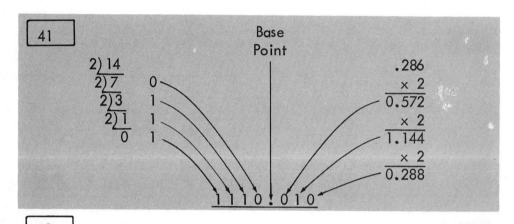

41

Base Point

```
2) 14
 2) 7    0
  2) 3   1
   2) 1  1
    0   1
```

1 1 1 0 ! 0 1 0

```
       .286
      ×  2
     0.572
      ×  2
     1.144
      ×  2
     0.288
```

63

```
2) 27
 2) 13   1
  2) 6   1
   2) 3  0
    2) 1 1
     0  1
```

Base Point

1 1 0 1 1 ! 0 1 1

```
       .429
      ×  2
     0.858
      ×  2
     1.716
      ×  2
     1.432
```

$$\frac{3}{7} = \frac{.4285}{7)3.0000} \quad or \quad .429$$

85

ⓐ
```
     1 1 . 1 1
   ×   1 0 . 1
     1 1 1 1
   1 1 1 1 0
 1 0 0 1 . 0 1 1
```

ⓑ
```
     1 1 . 1
   × 1 . 1 1
     1 1 1
     1 1 1
   1 0 1 0 1   Partial sum
     1 1 1
 1 1 0 . 0 0 1   Answer
```

204

20

To convert a DECIMAL NUMBER to a BINARY NUMBER:

1. <u>Convert</u> the WHOLE number.

2. <u>Convert</u> the FRACTIONAL number.

3. <u>Add</u> the TWO.

GO TO NEXT FRAME

42

Convert $11\frac{3}{4}$ to BINARY

64

Binary Arithmetic
with Mixed Numbers

GO TO NEXT FRAME

86

<u>Solve the following:</u>

      (a) $11.0\overline{)111.01}$ (b) $.10\overline{)1110}$

42

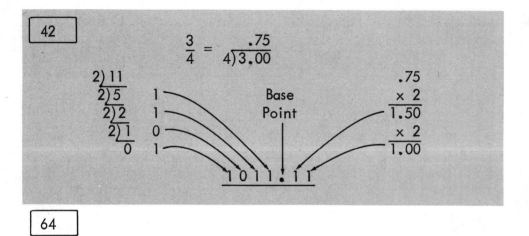

$$\frac{3}{4} = 4\overline{)3.00}^{.75}$$

64

86

@ 11.0)111.0.1 1 0.0
110
1 0 1

ⓑ .10)1110.00. 111 00.
10
11
10
10
10
00

A (subscript) tells the system in which the number is written.

   892_{10} is in the decimal system.
        (subscript)

   123_8 is in the octal system.
        (subscript)

   1001_2 is in the _____ system.
        (subscript)

43

Convert $15\frac{2}{3}$ to BINARY (compute to 3 places).

65

BINARY ARITHMETIC with Mixed Numbers is the same as DECIMAL ARITHMETIC with Mixed Numbers.

GO TO NEXT FRAME

87

Solve the following:

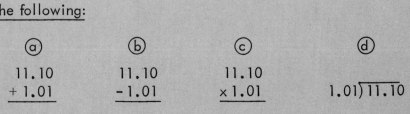

ⓐ	ⓑ	ⓒ	ⓓ
11.10	11.10	11.10	
+ 1.01	− 1.01	× 1.01	1.01⟌11.10

binary

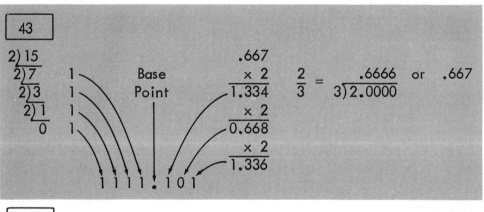

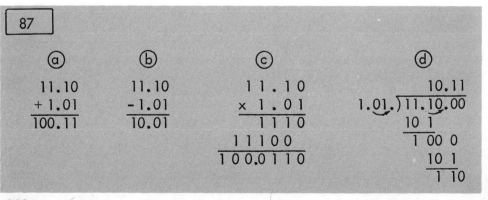

Let us REVIEW CONVERSION of WHOLE Numbers

To convert a DECIMAL Whole Number to a BINARY Whole Number

STEP I – Divide the DECIMAL number by ② → 2) 12

     and record the remainder (con-   2)6   0

     tinue to (zero)   2)3   0

                 2)1   1

STEP II – Sequence remainders   0   1

       GO TO NEXT FRAME   12 =   1 1 0 0

44

You have learned how to convert mixed DECIMAL numbers to BINARY.

You will now learn how to convert mixed BINARY Numbers to DECIMAL.

       GO TO NEXT FRAME

---

66   BINARY ADDITION and SUBTRACTION

Just as in Decimal addition and subtraction, Binary addition and sub-traction lines–up all the base points.

   ⓐ   Decimal   ⓑ   Binary

     835.32   110.10

    + 21.5   + 10.1

    ———— . —————   ———— . —————

88

You have just completed a course in COMPUTER NUMBERING SYS-TEMS AND BINARY ARITHMETIC.

       GO TO NEXT PAGE

22

44

66

(a) 856.82

(b) 1001.00

88

GO TO FRAME 23 ON PAGE 167

GO TO FRAME 45 ON PAGE 167

GO TO FRAME 67 ON PAGE 167

Review this course by reading <u>Chapter V</u> which is the <u>Summarized</u> <u>Reference</u>.

GO TO SUMMARIZED REFERENCE ON NEXT PAGE

NOTES

Chapter V   Summarized Reference

Chapter V is a summary of the course and is not programed. It can be used as a quick reference for obtaining information. Students who have completed this course should use the summarized reference to quickly recall forgotten information. If further clarification is needed, they can refer to the program itself. This summary encompasses the entire course: 1) the introduction, 2) conversion between systems, 3) binary arithmetic, and 4) fractional numbers.

NOW, TURN THE PAGE AND READ THE SUMMARIZED REFERENCE.

I Introduction-Numbering Systems

System	Symbols	Base
Decimal	0,1,2,3,4,5,6,7,8,9	10
Octal	0,1,2,3,4,5,6,7	8
Binary	0,1	2

II Conversion Between Systems

1. DECIMAL TO BINARY

Step 1 – Divide decimal number by binary base   2

Step 2 – Sequence remainders

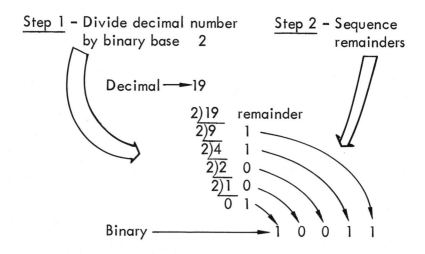

Decimal ⟶ 19

	remainder
2)19	
2)9	1
2)4	1
2)2	0
2)1	0
0	1

Binary ⟶ 1 0 0 1 1

2. DECIMAL TO OCTAL

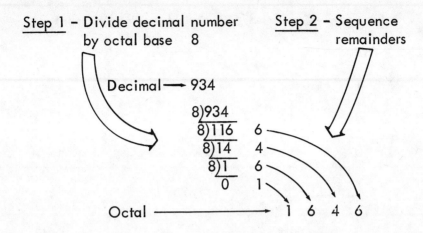

Step 1 – Divide decimal number by octal base 8

Step 2 – Sequence remainders

Decimal ⟶ 934

```
8)934
 8)116   6
  8)14   4
   8)1   6
     0   1
```

Octal ⟶ 1 6 4 6

3. BINARY TO DECIMAL

Example: Convert 1110 to the decimal equivalent

a. Expand: $1\ 1\ 1\ 0 = 0\,(2^0) + 1\,(2^1) + 1\,(2^2) + 1\,(2^3)$

b. Multiply: $= 0\,(1) + 1\,(2) + 1\,(4)\cdot + 1\,(8)$

$$= 0 \quad + 2 \quad + 4 \quad + 8$$

c. Add: $= 14$

Therefore: $1110_2 = 14_{10}$

4. OCTAL TO DECIMAL

Example: Convert 375 to the decimal equivalent

a. Expand: $3\ 7\ 5\ =\ 5\,(8^0) + 7\,(8^1) + 3\,(8^2)$

b. Multiply: $=\ 5\,(1)\ \ + 7\,(8)\ \ + 3\,(64)$

$=\ 5\ \ \ \ \ \ + 56\ \ \ \ + 192$

c. Add: $=\ 253$

Therefore: $375_8\ =\ 253_{10}$

5. BINARY TO OCTAL

Example: Convert 11001110 to the octal equivalent

11　　001　　110　　◁ Bracket every 3 digits

3　　　1　　　6　　◁ Decimal equivalent of bracketed digits

316$_8$　　◁ Octal equivalent of 11001110_2

6. OCTAL TO BINARY

Example: Convert 716 to the binary equivalent

3　　1　　6　　◁ Octal number

11　　001　　110　　◁ Binary equivalent of each octal digit

111001110　　◁ Binary equivalent of 316_8

7. BINARY CODED DECIMAL

Example:

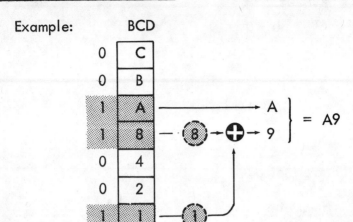

III Binary Arithmetic

---

1. BINARY ADDITION

$$0 + 0 = 0$$
$$1 + 0 = 1$$
$$0 + 1 = 1$$
$$1 + 1 = 10$$

Example:

```
  1  0  1  1  ←Augend
+        1  0  ←Addend
  ①
  1  1  0  1  ←Sum
```

2. BINARY SUBTRACTION

$$0 - 0 = 0$$
$$1 - 0 = 1$$
$$10 - 0 = 10$$
$$10 - 1 = 1$$
$$0 - 1 = 1 \quad \text{and borrow}$$

a. Borrow Method

Example:

```
        1
    0  10 10
  1  1  0  0  1  ←Minuend
 -        1  1  0  ←Subtrahend
  ─────────────────
  1  0  0  1  1  ←Difference
```

b. Complementing Method

(1) How to complement

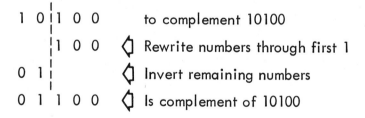

1 0 |1 0 0   to complement 10100

   |1 0 0   ◁ Rewrite numbers through first 1

0 1 | ◁ Invert remaining numbers

0 1 1 0 0   ◁ Is complement of 10100